YANKEE DOODLE'S COUSINS

YANKEE DOODLE'S COUSINS

ANNE MALCOLMSON

Illustrated by

Robert McCloskey

Houghton Mifflin Company · Boston

The Riverside Press Cambridge

The Riverside Press
CAMBRIDGE · MASSACHUSETTS
PRINTED IN THE U.S.A.

For E. L. B.

Preface

TO many of us who teach school the recent upsurge in
national feeling has posed a problem. This new con-
sciousness of the goodness of life in America is inevitable and
healthy. Never has there been so much need for an awareness
of democracy and its blessings as in these tragic days. But
how can we help our beloved ten-year-olds to an affectionate
pride in their country?

To a youngster who, for his own good, must live under an
authoritarian government-by-decree, whether of parent or
teacher, 'democracy' is very difficult to understand. To a
child whose personal geography is limited to a countryside
or a city neighborhood, America as a nation is something
incomprehensible.

The English youngsters are lucky in their national heroes.
They have King Arthur and Beowulf and Robin Hood to
fight for, each in his own way outrageously congenial to the
ten-year-old world. Our children have George Washington
and Abraham Lincoln, whose heroic qualities, magnificent
as they are, are essentially adult qualities. The Lone Ranger
is more at home in the imagination of a fifth-grader than is
either of these more worthy gentlemen.

Fortunately there is no need for frantic invention on our
part. We have a tremendous fund of American tradition and
folk literature on which to draw, but until recently it has

been denied its proper place in the cultural sun. We teachers who have been educated in the East are too much in the habit of looking to England and Europe as the source of all literary merit, and have snubbed American folk literature as 'roughneck,' or at best given it the doubtful honor of being considered 'interesting local color.'

The few stories which have risen above the snubs to become American classics are grand to read aloud to children. Unfortunately, because of rhetorical style and 'literary' vocabulary, most of these make 'tough going' for the child who tries to read them to himself. Even the Uncle Remus stories, told in dialect, demand a mature reading skill.

Within the past twenty years the American scene and the American idiom have come into their own in literature for adults. There have been a number of excellent books and plays about our national folk heroes. Older boys and girls have been introduced to the giants of the New World. But for younger children there is still a lamentable lack of reading matter that presents traditional American lore without apology or condescension.

The yarns that have grown out of young America belong to children, as much by right of sympathy as by right of heritage. Paul Bunyan and Pecos Bill are ten years old at heart. Their humor, their wildly romantic exaggerations, their quixotic naïveté, their lack of self-consciousness, and their hard-headed adaptability to circumstances — all these are qualities of the average fifth-grader.

When Mike Fink yells, 'I'm a Salt River roarer! I'm a ring-tailed squealer!', he's a blood brother of the bantam-weight quarterback who warbles, 'C'mon, men, let's mow 'em down.' He's the blood brother also of one Robin Hood

Preface

who invited the Bishop of Hereford to dine on the king's venison and made him dance for his dinner.

But to get back to the problem of making America and the things it stands for come alive to the fifth grade, I can't help thinking that one way of going about it is to introduce a few of our Yankee heroes to their descendants. Paul Bunyan's Real Americans can help our children identify themselves with the working, democratic, industrial civilization that is America.

This collection of stories is by no means an answer to the problem. The only virtue it may have is that it's an attempt to present a scattering of Real American heroes in a book which younger children can read to themselves. Instead of collecting material at first hand throughout the country, I've done most of my research in the files of the Library of Congress, picking other people's brains. So far as possible, I've tried to acknowledge my debts. And these are legion.

I should like to make grateful acknowledgment —

To Paul R. Beath for permission to use material from 'Febold Feboldson';

To Josef Berger for permission to use the story of 'Ichabod Paddock' from his book 'Cape Cod Pilot,' published by the Modern Pilgrim Press, Provincetown;

To C. E. Brown for permission to use material from his book 'Paul Bunyan and Tony Beaver Tales,' Madison, Wisconsin;

For the story of 'The Golden Cities of Cibola,' which is adapted from the original in Hallenbeck's 'Legends of the Spanish Southwest,' by permission of the publishers, The Arthur H. Clark Company;

To Mr. J. Frank Dobie, of the University of Texas, for permission to use his material about the 'White Mustang,' and

Preface

for permission to use material from the article 'Jean Lafitte,' by E. G. Littlejohn, published in The Texas Folk Lore Society Publication, No. III;

To Doubleday, Doran & Company, Inc., for permission to reprint the first and last stanzas of the 'Stormalong' ballad from 'Iron Men and Wooden Ships,' by Frank Shay;

For the use of material from 'The Hurricane's Children,' by Carl Carmer, copyright, 1937, adapted by permission of Farrar & Rinehart, Inc., publishers;

To the Nebraska Writers' Project for permission to use material about Antoine Barada and The Gran Quivira from 'Nebraska Folklore';

For the quotation, 'Sunrise in His Pocket,' reprinted from 'Davy Crockett,' by Constance Rourke, by permission of Harcourt, Brace & Company, publishers;

To Mr. Lucien Harris for permission to use material contained in the stories of 'The Tar Baby' and 'The Deluge,' from 'Uncle Remus, His Songs and Sayings,' by Joel Chandler Harris;

To Henry Holt & Company, Inc., for permission to use material from 'Mike Fink,' by Blair and Meine;

For material which has been adapted from 'Paul Bunyan,' by James Stevens, by permission and special arrangement with Alfred A. Knopf, Inc., authorized publishers;

To J. B. Lippincott Company, of East Washington Square, Philadelphia, Pennsylvania, for permission to use the stories of 'The Gift of Saint Nicholas,' adapted from 'American Myths and Legends,' by Charles M. Skinner, and 'Why the Negro Works Harder than the White Man,' from 'Mules and Men,' by Zora N. Hurston;

To Longmans, Green & Company, Inc., for permission to retell the story of 'The Mule Humans,' from 'Tall Tales of the Kentucky Mountains,' by Percy MacKaye;

Preface

To the University of North Carolina Press for permission to use material from 'John Henry,' by Guy Johnson;

To the University of Pennsylvania for permission to use material from 'Minstrels of the Mine Patch,' by George Korson;

To Albert Whitman & Company, of Chicago, Illinois, for permission to use material from 'Pecos Bill,' by James Cloyd Bowman;

For permission to retell the stories of Stormalong and Kemp Morgan from 'Here's Audacity,' by Frank Shay; copyright, 1930, by him;

To Miss Margaret Gaskill, for her generous advice on problems of reading level and vocabulary;

And, of course, to my husband, for his patience during dull winter evenings when his wife was trying to be an 'author.'

Contents

THE EAST

THE SOUTH

THE MISSISSIPPI VALLEY

Contents

THE WEST

The East

John Darling

I

MANY, many stories have been told about the Erie
Canal. Of them all, the one I like the most is the story
of John Augustus Caesar Darling. John Darling probably
had many other impressive names. But his friends called
him John for short.

He wasn't much as a little boy. He lived on a farm in upper New York State. He helped his father feed the pig and
milk the cow. In the spring he went into the maple woods
and helped hang the sugar buckets on their hooks. He
pitched hay in the summer and gathered apples in the fall.
That is about all we know about him then.

But as he grew older he became more interesting. He was
about eleven years old when he first became important. His
father sent him out to the field. He hitched the team of steers
to the old wooden plow. As he moved up and down the furrow, he sang himself a song — a song that he loved dearly

'I've got a mule and her name is Sal,
Fifteen miles on the Erie Canal.
She's a good old worker and a good old pal,
Fifteen miles on the Erie Canal.'

Yankee Doodle's Cousins

It was a long song, with more verses than you can count on the fingers of your right hand. Sometimes the verses changed. Sal wasn't always a mule. She was occasionally a cook, 'the very best cook on the Erie Canal.'

As he sang to himself and to the steers, young John Augustus Caesar dreamed of the future. Some day he would own a boat. He would ride up and down the Erie Canal, like a king on his barge.

All of a sudden, John woke up from his dream. He stopped singing. Right ahead of him loomed a big stump, at least six feet high. It was too late to turn away. Already the oxen had passed it, one on each side. Here were John and his plow, about to be stuck on the stump.

John Darling shut his eyes. He whipped his oxen and they pushed ahead. The old plow went right through the stump, with John after it. Yes, the stump split in two as clean as a whistle. John could hardly believe his eyes. He turned around to take another look at the stump. Just as he did so, the two halves rose up from the ground and fitted themselves together.

Now, things like that don't happen to a plain ordinary farm boy. John Augustus Caesar Darling rubbed his eyes. He went back and felt the stump to make sure. There it was, as solid as a brick wall. Only magic could have done such a thing.

His family laughed at him when he told them what had happened. They didn't believe it at all. John himself, however, knew that he had had a sign. Some day he would be an important man. There was no doubt in his mind about that.

The following summer his remarkable powers were proved to his family. Mr. Darling, his father, noticed that the roof was leaking. He put the boys to work whittling shingles

2

John Darling

from pine boards. Then he propped a ladder against the side of the house. It was John's job to nail the shingles to the roof.

Unhappily, the weather was bad. A fog had rolled over the whole of upper New York State from Lake Ontario, as thick as pea soup. Even so, John put on his raincoat and climbed the ladder. He climbed to the very top and carried his shingles with him. One by one he fitted them in place and nailed them together.

All day long he worked. Shingle upon shingle, he hammered until the roof was finished. He had, in fact, made a whole new roof. He couldn't see it all at once to admire it because the fog was so thick.

When he climbed down again the sun came out and chased away the fog. Then John discovered his wonderful mistake. He had hammered the shingles together twenty feet above the ridge-pole of the house. There hung his roof in mid-air. He had laid it on top of the fog.

As a grown man, John Darling first went to work as a 'sugarbush' man. In other words, he had a stand of maple-sugar trees. He loved to go out into the woods and to tap the trees when the sap began to run. Into each he inserted a short pipe, and under each pipe he hung a bucket. Then, when the sap had collected in the buckets, he took them home. He boiled and boiled until his kettles were sticky with delicious maple syrup.

He was particularly fond of maple syrup on buckwheat cakes. All winter long he had his favorite dish for breakfast. In the spring he cut off his long beard. His first wife used to collect his whiskers and boil them down in the big kettle Usually she boiled out several gallons of syrup that had stuck to the beard during John's breakfasts.

3

Yankee Doodle's Cousins

The thing that finally discouraged him from the maple-sugar business was the mosquito. As you know, mosquitoes love sweets. They used to hover around Darling's maple trees. They were as large as airplanes. Their buzz-buzz-buzz sounded as loud as the hum of a sawmill. They stung the farm hands when they came to collect the sap. They stung even John himself.

At last John thought of a way to be rid of them. His sap pans were large iron kettles. Into one of these he put some pure maple sugar. Then he turned it upside down under one of his trees. He hid himself inside, his big hammer in his hand. Sure enough! The mosquitoes smelled it. They came from miles around to nibble at the sugar. But the iron kettle was in their way. Buzz-buzz-buzz! They put their stingers to work. They bored through the iron of the kettle until they reached the soft sweet sugar beneath it.

John was too smart for them. As each stinger bored through the iron, John came up with his hammer. He flattened the mosquito's bill against the inside of the kettle.

Within an hour all the mosquitoes were safely fastened to the sap pan. They were so angry they buzzed like a hangar full of planes. But there was nothing they could do about it. At last they lifted their wings and off they flew. They took John Darling's sap pan with them, firmly fixed to their bills.

Before long, John Augustus Caesar Darling tired of farming. The 'Erie Canal' song ran through his head until it nearly drove him mad.

> 'Low bridge, everybody down!
> Low bridge, for we're going through a town,
> And you'll always know your neighbor,
> You'll always know your pal,
> If you ever navigated on the Erie Canal.'

4

John Darling

You can see for yourself how John must have felt. As he followed the plow he couldn't help singing, 'Low bridge.' Even the steers thought he was a little silly. There wasn't a bridge anywhere near the cornfield.

At last he couldn't stand it any longer. He sold his farm and his sugar trees and went to Albany. There he bought himself a canal boat, a beautiful boat. He painted it white and named it the *Erie Queen*. He fitted up the captain's cabin with his favorite possessions. This was a home after his own heart.

John filled up the hold of the *Erie Queen* with shoes and watches and plows and started off for Buffalo. His old horse plodded along the tow-path, pulling the boat. Sometimes John walked beside the horse smoking his pipe. Sometimes he sat on deck in the sun, his big face shining with pleasure.

It was perfectly all right for him to sing the Canal song now. After all, you don't feel silly bawling out, 'Low bridge, everybody down,' when there is a low bridge ahead of you.

Up and down the Canal slid the *Erie Queen*. When she reached Buffalo, John unloaded his watches and shoes and plows. He sold them to the pioneers who were moving west into Ohio and Indiana. Sometimes he sold them to the captains of the Lake ships. They took them even farther west, up through the Great Lakes to Wisconsin and Minnesota to the Swedes and Norwegians.

When John had sold his wares, he bought others. From the Lake captains and Western farmers he bought lumber and coal and hay. Then he and the *Erie Queen* headed back to Buffalo. Here he sold his cargo to the Eastern merchants.

Back and forth, back and forth, from Albany to Buffalo, back and forth moved John Darling, as happy as a king. He

5

John Darling

stopped at the locks to chat with the lock-keepers while they raised his boat into a higher level, or lowered it into a lower one. He knew all the other boatmen by name. He swapped stories with them.

One of the stories was about a boatman who had taken his barge down to New York Harbor. There in the harbor he had found a dead whale. He mounted the whale on his barge and scooped out the inside. He cut windows through the ribs and propped the mouth open to make a door. The whale's interior was fixed up as a cabin. People came flocking to see the boatman's prize. He charged them two pennies apiece to look around inside. Soon he was very rich.

To cook his meals John Darling hired a young woman named Sal. He claimed she was the original 'Sal' of the song, 'the very best cook on the Erie Canal.' She made buckwheat cakes that were as light as goose down.

She was more than a good cook, however. She was a remarkable woman. Sal was over six feet tall, freckled, cross-eyed, and twenty-three years old. She was indeed a daisy. Furthermore, she had red hair, so red it outshone the glory of the sunsets. It glowed like a whole cluster of fireflies. In fact, on dark nights, John had Sal sit in the bow of the boat. He used her for a headlight.

Before long, John Darling was completely in love. The only thing he needed to make his happiness perfect was Sal. Sal, however, had many other beaux. Every boatman, every lock-keeper was in love with her, too. Whenever John asked her to marry him, she said, 'No!'

At last he persuaded her to give him a chance. She arranged to hold a contest. All the Canalmen were great fishermen. On quiet afternoons they liked to trail their fishing lines over the sides of their boats. Often they caught enough

7

pickerel or perch for their suppers. Sal agreed that she would marry the man who caught the most fish on a certain day.

All her other suitors, of course, were told about the contest. They fixed up their fishing tackle. They brushed their beards and combed their mustaches, and put on their best store clothes. On the proper day they came together at the meeting place.

The contest began at midnight and lasted until the following midnight. Twenty-four hours in which to catch a bride!

John Augustus Caesar Darling, handsome in his new suit, sat at the bow of the *Erie Queen*. Up and down the Canal, as far as one could see, were the boats of his rivals. Each of the men held a fishing line in his hand.

Unfortunately, the other suitors had good luck. They reeled in their lines, one after another, until their decks were piled with fish. Poor old John had not a nibble. He jiggled his fishing pole, but nothing happened. He sat perfectly still. Nothing happened. By noon he had not a fish to his name.

By sundown the other suitors were growing tired. They had been hauling in bass and perch all day long, and were ready to quit. Most of them gave up and started to count their catch. But not John. He sat on the deck of the *Erie Queen*, sadly holding his fishing pole. His big tank was still empty. Not a fish.

Meanwhile, Sal had been watching the contest from the bank. She saw John and his empty tank. She felt sorry for him, because she really wanted him to win.

As soon as it was dark she climbed aboard his barge. John was surprised to see her. Her beautiful red hair shone like the tail of a comet. It lit up the whole Canal.

This gave John an idea. 'Put your head over the side,' he

said softly to Sal. She did as he told her. The light from her hair gleamed out across the black water to the other bank. In its path swam a school of fat black bass.

The fish were attracted by the light. They acted like moths around the flame of a candle. One by one they jumped into John's boat. They didn't wait for him to catch them on his line.

'Now put your head over the other side,' John whispered to Sal. He was afraid to startle the fish. There, in the path of the light, swam a school of pickerel. One by one they, too, jumped out of the water onto the deck of the *Erie Queen*. They didn't even wait to be invited.

With Sal's help, John Darling soon had his hold full of squirming, fine fish. The decks also were piled high with them. When at last the village clock sounded midnight, he and Sal were knee deep in perch and bass and bullheads.

The judging took place in the courthouse. The other Canalmen swaggered in with their catches. Each was sure that he had won Sal's hand. Imagine the dismay when John came in. The judges counted his fish. Without any question at all, they had to admit that he had won the contest. Sal tried to look surprised when he claimed her. But everyone could see that she was more pleased than surprised.

They were soon married. John Darling took his bride to Niagara Falls for their honeymoon. When they returned to the *Erie Queen*, the neighbors gathered and gave them a big party. They had songs and dancing and a fish fry and maple syrup and buckwheat cakes. It was a great success.

From then on, John's happiness was complete. He used to sing out his favorite song at the top of his lungs. People two miles away could tell he was coming when they heard him shout, 'Low bridge, everybody down.'

Yankee Doodle's Cousins

He changed the verse a little, though. Instead of singing,
'I've got a mule, and her name is Sal,' he sang,

> 'I've got a wife, and her name is Sal,
> Fifteen miles on the Erie Canal.
> She's a good old worker and a good old pal,
> The very best cook on the Erie Canal.'

The Gift of Saint Nicholas

2

THREE hundred years ago in the little city of New Amsterdam lived a young cobbler named Claas. A fortunate young fellow indeed was Claas. He had a lovely brick house with a garden, a big pond full of fat white geese, a thriving trade, and a pretty wife whose name was Anitje. He had worked hard for these blessings from the first bleak day when he landed on the shores of the New World, an orphan boy from Holland. He now was a rich man, rich enough to wear eight pairs of breeches at once.

The only dark cloud in his sky was Roeloffsen, the burgomaster, an old miser who had long been in love with Anitje. As the richest old bachelor in the town, he had expected her to marry him without any question. When she married the poor cobbler boy, the burgomaster's pride was hurt. He swore that he should have his revenge. Whenever Claas and Anitje walked out in their Sunday clothes, with their family of fat Dutch children toddling behind them, he hid behind the heavy curtains of his house and said terrible things.

At last his ugly thoughts were put into deeds. He taught
the village blacksmith to make hobnails for the townspeo-
ple's boots. These nails made a dreadful racket as they clattered over the brick streets. But they kept the boots from
wearing out. The boots wore so long that poor Claas had
very little business as a cobbler. He had a very hard time of
it to make ends meet.

This was not enough for the black-hearted burgomaster,
however. Claas and his Anitje still lived in their fine brick
house and walked out on Sundays in their handsome clothes.
Roeloffsen had to think of something else.

Soon he knew what to do. As an officer of the city he
ordered a new street to be built. This street ran right through
the middle of Claas's pond. The city builders came and
drained the pond. Poor Claas had to sell his beloved geese.
This was a great blow to him, because the eggs he sold at the
marketplace helped make up for the boots he was unable to
sell.

But this was not the worst of it. As Claas sat by his fire
sorrowing for the loss of his geese, he had visitors. These
were men from the city council. Since the road ran through
his land, they said, he should pay for its building. They demanded fifty pieces of gold for this purpose. Fifty pieces of
gold! That was all Claas had tucked away in his teapot.

Claas and Anitje had to work harder than ever to keep
their family fed and clothed. They sold vegetables from
their little garden and managed to make themselves a fair
living. Then came the jealous burgomaster. He built another road, through the middle of Claas's garden patch this
time. Once again the poor cobbler had to rob his teapot of
the vegetable money in order to pay for this road.

And so it went. Every time Claas made a little money, the

The Gift of Saint Nicholas

burgomaster built a new road and made him pay for it. Before long, he had to sell his fine house. No longer could he afford to wear eight pairs of breeches, nor Anitje her twelve petticoats. The little family was poor. They had sold all their belongings except a bare few. They lived in a miserable little cottage with only a dirt floor.

The wicked old burgomaster at last was satisfied. He danced with joy when he saw how low the cobbler had fallen. This would show the people of New Amsterdam that no orphan boy could outdo the wealthy Heer Roeloffsen!

On Christmas Eve, as the burgomaster was enjoying his fine dinner, Claas and Anitje and their children sat huddled before the fireplace in their little cottage. The very last log burned on the hearth and gave out little heat at best. Their cupboard, like Old Mother Hubbard's, was bare. After their supper of bread and cheese, not a crumb remained. A poor Christmas this would be. No presents, no blazing fire, not even a dinner!

Of all their possessions, only two treasures remained. One was the Bible which Claas's mother had given him long ago. It was bound in beautiful leather and held shut with silver clasps. Claas was tempted to take off these clasps and sell them. They might bring him enough money to provide a Christmas for his children.

No! said Anitje. To sell the clasps from a Bible would be wicked. He should never think of doing such a thing. Better it would be to starve than to feast on the sale of holy things.

The other treasure which remained was a pipe. This was a special, lovely pure meerschaum pipe which to Claas had a magic meaning. As a little boy, leaving his home for the New World, he had found the pipe in his stocking. Where it had come from he could not tell. He was sure it was a present from the good Saint Nicholas himself.

The thought of selling this treasure nearly broke his heart. Even so, it was better than the thought of selling his mother's silver clasps. He reached down into the family chest and took out his beloved meerschaum. Sadly he rubbed it against his trousers and watched it gleam in the firelight.

As he rubbed it the cottage door swung open and a blast of cold air filled the room. There before the fire stood a fat little stranger, about three feet tall. He was dripping with snow, and icicles hung from his shaggy eyebrows and his long white beard.

'Br-r-r!' muttered the stranger crossly. 'It's a wonder you wouldn't answer the door when a traveler knocks. Fine manners, I must say, on a night like this!'

All thoughts of the pipe were forgotten as Claas and Anitje stared at their visitor. The children scrambled to hide under the bed. Only their bright blue eyes shone out from behind the curtains.

'Well, come along! Come along!' went on the visitor, growing more angry every minute. 'Don't stand there! The least you can do is to put another log on the fire so that I can warm myself. Can't you see I'm half frozen?'

'I-I-I-I'm very sorry, sir,' admitted Claas, finding his tongue at last, 'but there is no other log to put on the fire. You're very welcome to warm yourself at our poor hearth.'

'Well, then,' snapped the stranger, 'send one of those ragamuffins out to the woodshed. I'm freezing, I tell you!' He glared at the children, who pushed themselves farther back under the bed hangings.

'Oh, sir!' cried Anitje, 'if only we had more wood in the

shed we would gladly fetch it for you. But, alas, this is our last stick. We have no more to keep ourselves warm.'

'Humph!' snorted the little fellow. 'That's very careless of you. But what must be, must be.' With that he cracked the fine cane he carried over his knee. It broke into several pieces. These he tossed onto the coals. As they struck the fire, something wonderful happened. Each of the pieces of the cane changed into a big birch log. The dark coals blazed up and soon the room was dancing with the light of a huge fire.

'That's better,' muttered the stranger. 'Upon my life, I thought I should turn to an icicle for all you cared.'

The children crept out from their hiding place to gape at the magic blaze. Claas and Anitje rubbed their eyes.

'And now, I suppose, you're going to let me starve to death, too!' sneered the visitor, looking in the direction of the cupboard. 'It's a wonder you wouldn't invite me to have some supper. I haven't eaten since this morning.'

Tears came to Anitje's eyes. 'Oh, sir, whoever you may be, we should indeed be happy to give you our last crumb. But,' she sobbed, 'we have nothing to eat in the house. We ate our last scrap of cheese for our evening meal.'

'That was certainly rude of you,' barked the funny little man. 'Here I come, after a hard day's tramp over the mountains, through wind and rain and snow! You say you have no fire to warm me! You say you have no bread to feed me! My dear lady, I know better. Your shelves are heaped with cakes and apples. And if that's not roast goose I smell cooking, I'll eat my beard!'

Without thinking, the whole family stopped to sniff. Why, they did smell roast goose! And cabbage and onion and mince pie and pumpkin! These delicious smells were fairly bursting from the oven door. They looked quickly at the cupboard. Its shelves were groaning under bowls of apples and pears and platters of cakes and cookies. The water jug was filled to the brim with sweet cider.

'Don't stand there, don't stand there like a forest of trees!' shouted the stranger. 'Can't you see I'm dying of hunger? Get me something to eat and be quick about it. No food, indeed! Why, there's a whole feast in that oven. Put it on the table.'

Not knowing whether to be overjoyed or frightened, Claas and Anitje set the table and drew it before the fire. They opened the wide door of the oven. There indeed were the goose and the vegetables and the pies they smelled.

At the sight of the richly spread table, the children forgot their shyness. Hungrily they feasted. But none of them ate so much as did their visitor. Time and again he passed back his plate for another drumstick. An ordinary goose has only two legs, but this one sprouted a new one whenever the little man passed his plate.

When at last the fat little stranger had had enough and the buttons had begun to burst from Claas's coat, the table was cleared away. No longer did the visitor snap angrily at his hosts. He leaned back in his chair and lit his pipe. A twinkle appeared in his eye and he patted the children's blond heads. For an hour he sat talking pleasantly with the happy family, telling strange and marvelous stories of distant lands. But not once did he tell them who he was.

At the stroke of midnight he got up from his chair. 'I must be off!' he exclaimed. 'Thank you indeed for a pleasant evening and a delicious dinner.' He turned to Claas. 'Don't ever sell that pipe!' he shouted.

With that, a gust of wind down the chimney filled the

whole room with smoke. Before the family could open their
smarting eyes again, the stranger was gone without so much
as a good-bye.

In the morning Claas was awakened by a great hammering
at his door. There was Burgomaster Roeloffsen and a party
of soldiers. 'We have come to arrest you!' they screamed.
'You are a wizard, a witch, a magician. You are a disgrace
to the city of New Amsterdam.'

Poor Claas didn't know what to make of it. Why should
anyone call him a wizard? He was nothing but a poor cobbler who had had a lovely dream.

'Come!' roared the burgomaster. 'Open the door and let
us in. We shall have no wizards in our city!'

As he slowly awakened, Claas looked about him. The
wretched little cottage had disappeared. He was standing in
the hall of a great house. The walls were hung with silks,
and from the cupboards shone silver platters and copper
bowls. He looked timidly out of the window. Around him
spread wide lawns and gardens and in the distance glimmered
the ice of a huge pond.

'Open up, I say,' bellowed the burgomaster. 'Open up in
the name of the law. We have come to take you to jail as you
deserve.' Claas opened the door. In poured the soldiers.

'Aha!' screamed Heer Roeloffsen, his face red with anger.
'Seize him! Seize the witch! He has not only changed his
cottage to a fine estate. He has filled his chests with gold.'

Before the astonished Claas the burgomaster lifted the lid
of a chest. The great box was full to the top with pieces of
money.

'You thief! You robber! I'll...' But before he could finish his sentence, a pair of invisible hands clapped themselves
over his mouth. More hands which could not be seen grabbed

the soldiers. Then came an awful whacking and thrashing as the unseen arms paddled the burgomaster and his party with unseen switches.

'Ouch! Help! Stop it!' yelled Roeloffsen. But the paddling went on. The soldiers ran down the path to the main road and headed away from town, crying and yelling and trying to defend themselves from the blows of the unseen paddlers.

That was the last ever seen of the jealous burgomaster. Claas and his family lived on in their fine new home, never wanting for food or warmth. How their good fortune had come they did not know. The only clue they had was a piece of paper slipped under the door. It said simply, 'Don't ever sell that pipe.'

Captain Kidd

3

FAR out on the ocean wanders a ghostly ship, its sails
shimmering in the dark of night. Sailors have seen it
often, and have heard the sad howling of the wind through
its rigging. Sometimes when the wind is right they can hear
the mournful song of its unhappy captain, who paces the
deck bemoaning his fate.

'Oh, my name was William Kidd, when I sailed, when I sailed,
My name was William Kidd, when I sailed.
My name was William Kidd,
God's laws I did forbid,
And so wickedly I did, when I sailed.'

On and on he sings, verse after verse, telling the whole grim
story of his life.

In 1695 Lord Bellomont called Captain William Kidd into
his office in London. Shortly before the noble lord had received the King's message. He was to be the new governor
of the colonies of New York and New England. It was his
job to rid the seas of pirates and French privateers who

preyed on the trade between the New World and the Old. He needed able men, of course, to help him carry out his orders. Who was more able to do this than the famous Captain Kidd?

For many years Kidd had sailed the seas in His Majesty's service. He was known as one of the best shipmasters on the Atlantic. Furthermore, he had already captured a number of privateers in the French wars. Lord Bellomont was certain that he had made a good choice.

But the captain hemmed and hawed. After all, fighting pirates was a dangerous thing to do for a living, and he had his wife and children to think about. They were waiting for him in his fine home in New York. How he longed to see them! Captain Kidd was no ordinary buccaneer; he was a peaceful, home-loving citizen.

Lord Bellomont tried everything he could think of to persuade the captain. He mentioned the honor and the glory that would be his. He begged him to think of his duty to his king. Still the sailor said, 'No.'

At last the new governor, who had made up his mind to have Kidd, called in the Lords of the Admiralty. They had the final say. Unless the captain would agree to fight the pirates, his ship would be taken from him and he would be in disgrace. This was too much for William Kidd. He had to say 'Yes.'

When Kidd arrived once more in New York Harbor in a fine new ship *Adventure*, the whole town turned out to meet him. Lord Bellomont, who had crossed the ocean before him, was there to welcome him as a hero. The people shouted and waved flags in his honor. On the dock stood his wife and children, proud of their husband and father.

The glory could not last, however. As soon as he had

fitted his ship with supplies for a long voyage and had signed on an extra crew, Captain Kidd had to set about his business. Up and down the coast he sailed, looking for his enemies. The pirates, who had heard of his coming, had all run for cover. Not a buccaneer could he find!

He set his sails for the West Indies and prowled in and out among the islands, still looking in vain for pirates. Back and forth across the Caribbean, along the Spanish Main where they liked to prey on treasure ships, he hunted them. But the unhappy captain was out of luck. No pirates!

He became homesick, thinking about his family in New York. The crew became bored, thinking of the buccaneers that didn't show up. Tempers began to snap on board the *Adventure*. To keep his men from quarreling, Kidd sailed across the Atlantic and around Africa to the Indian Ocean. This was another favorite place for the Jolly Roger, the black flag of the ocean robbers.

But in the Indian Ocean he couldn't find what he was looking for. Kidd had permission from the British Government to attack the French, because the two countries were at war. Not even a French ship sailed across his path.

At last a caravel showed itself across the horizon. Without waiting for their captain's permission, Kidd's crew got ready for battle. They were tired of sailing without capturing anything. Here came a fleet of ships, full of treasure from the Indies, waiting to be captured. Poor Captain! It was the British East Indian fleet, bringing gold from the colonies to the mother country. He had no right to attack his own country's navy.

Nevertheless the crew opened fire. They had no chance against so many ships, but all they cared about was a chance to fight someone. Before nightfall they had to run for their lives. They had captured none of the treasure. All they had gotten was the bad name of 'Pirate.'

From then on, things went from bad to worse. Here was Kidd made a pirate against his will!

Some weeks later the *Adventure* met the *Royal Captain*, another British ship. Captain Kidd knew that word of his attack on the gold fleet would soon reach England. He had to do something to clear his name. So he invited the officers of the *Royal Captain* on board his ship and entertained them with a fine feast. He was going to explain to them what had happened.

But while the officers of the two ships were dining together in a friendly manner, the crew of the *Adventure* once more rose against their master. They tried to capture the *Royal Captain*. In his anger Kidd threw a bucket at William Moore, the ringleader of the mutineers. It struck him on the head and the surly sailor fell to the deck, dead.

The other ship got away, but even so Kidd was in a pickle. He was not only a pirate, he was a murderer.

Instead of giving himself up to the British Navy and explaining what had happened, Captain Kidd ran away to Madagascar. This great island off the coast of Africa was a hotbed of piracy. In her ports lay the very ships Kidd had started out to catch. From their masts floated shamelessly the Jolly Roger. Swarthy, cruel-faced men with gay clothes and gold ear-rings swaggered through the streets. They boasted openly of the prizes they had taken, and no one paid any attention to them.

What a pleasant life these bandits seemed to lead! They had money in their pockets, and chests full of silks and jewels in their cabins. They feasted like kings on foods and wines brought from the four corners of the earth.

Captain Kidd

Culliford, the worst robber of the oceans, was in port when Kidd arrived. He was the very one Lord Bellomont had been most anxious to capture. Many a British man-o'-war had he sent to Davy Jones's Locker. But Kidd did not arrest him. He had dinner with him, instead. When the party was over, unhappy Captain Kidd hauled down the red, white, and blue flag of Great Britain and hoisted the black skull-and-bones of the pirate. He had become Culliford's partner.

For several years the new sea-robber roamed the Indian Ocean. He captured a large Armenian trader, the *Quedagh Merchant*. She was much larger than the *Adventure*, with more room for loot in her hold; so he sent her crew to the bottom, moved his crew and his treasure aboard, and set fire to his own ship.

To all outward appearances, Kidd was now a true pirate. He preyed on any ship that crossed his path, regardless of her flag. Proudly he flew the Jolly Roger, and ran into port in Madagascar to feast and swagger with his new friend Culliford. But at heart he was sad. He longed to see his wife and his children. He thought often of the sorrow he had caused them, of the shame they must feel for his disgrace.

His crew, too, bloodthirsty as they were, were growing tired of the pirate's trade. The *Merchant's* hold was full of gold. Why shouldn't they return to their homes? Each of them had money enough to live in luxury for years to come.

So Kidd started home. He sailed first to the West Indies. Here he planned to send a message to Lord Bellomont, explaining his misfortune and begging the governor's forgiveness. He thought he could say that the ships he had captured were French, and everything would be all right.

Little did he know what lay in store for him! No sooner had he reached the West Indies than he learned the truth.

Yankee Doodle's Cousins

The British Government had set a price on his head. He was not only a pirate, he was a murderer in their eyes. He could hope for no forgiveness from Bellomont or from anyone else.

In spite of this turn of affairs, he decided to take a chance. He bought a little sloop, the *Antonia*, and put aboard her a small part of his treasure. The remainder he left on the *Quedagh Merchant*, in charge of his chief officer, and ordered her into a secret cove to hide out until his return. Then he took the *Antonia* north.

He stopped first in Delaware Bay. This seemed to be a safe harbor in which to bury some of his treasure. Hardly had he placed a chest in the ground, however, before a party of passers-by noticed him. They recognized him at once. They set off for Philadelphia to warn the colonies that Kidd had returned.

He dared stay at anchor no longer. He moved to Long Island Sound. Here the *Antonia* hid each night in a different cove, while Kidd tried to reach Lord Bellomont. He managed to have his wife brought to him under the cover of night. She was broken-hearted by the notices which proclaimed her husband an outlaw. She was sure he was an honest man and promised to help him return to the governor's favor.

Nevertheless Lord Bellomont refused to see him and to listen to his story. If Kidd set foot on American soil, he should be arrested as a common thief. This was all the governor would promise.

Then the captain tried a different line. He picked out the finest silks and jewels in his chest and sent them to Lady Bellomont. Perhaps they would soften her heart and she would plead for him with her husband. Alas for Kidd! Lady Bellomont kept the jewels, but she refused to help him.

Captain Kidd

After many weeks, word came that the governor would see him. Bellomont had gone to Boston. If Kidd would come to him there, he would listen to the pirate's tale.

Light-hearted, Captain Kidd sailed to Boston. Dressed in his finest he walked up Beacon Street to the governor's offices. Alas! He never reached them. The message had been a trap. Before he knew it, he was in chains, bound for London and the Execution Dock.

The Lords of the Admiralty gave him no mercy. Like any common outlaw he was sentenced to death. Up over the Thames River, from which he had sailed proudly six years before, swung his body — a warning to would-be pirates.

Very little of his treasure was ever found. Some people believed for a time that he had buried it in the sands of Long Island and Cape Cod. But all the hardy souls who tried to dig it up were frightened away by strange ghosts who screeched and moaned and flapped their pale arms at the diggers. Strange Money-Lights, little balls of fire which rose from the earth, kept away others.

All that was left of the unhappy captain was his ghostly ship and his song.

> 'Farewell, the raging main, I must die, I must die,
> Farewell, the raging main, I must die.
> Farewell, the raging main,
> To Turkey, France and Spain,
> I shall ne'er see you again, I must die.'

Joe Magarac

4

STEVE MESTROVICH worked at the open hearth in the Hunkietown steel mill. For an old man he was very strong. He boasted that in his youth he had been the strongest worker in the steel counties.

The pride of his life, however, was his daughter Mary. Mary's eyes were as blue as cornflowers. Her hair was as blonde as molasses taffy. On Sunday afternoons, all the young men of Hunkietown came to call on her.

As her friends knew well, Mary was in love with Pete Pussick. But in the custom of Slovakia, from which Steve had come, a girl had nothing to say about her marriage. Her father decided that for her. It had always been that way.

Steve, of course, wanted Mary to be happy. But it never occurred to him that she might wish to pick out her own husband. Furthermore, he had once sworn a solemn vow that his son-in-law would have to prove himself the strongest young man in the Allegheny Valley.

On Mary's seventeenth birthday, her parents decided it

was time for her to have a husband. Steve made his plans. He invited the steel workers from all the Pennsylvania mills to come to a party. He sent his invitations to Homestead and to Bethlehem and to Johnstown, as well as to Hunkietown.

He sent to Pittsburgh for the refreshments, for soda pop and ice cream. Mrs. Mestrovich baked pies and cakes until her kitchen was full. Steve collected the materials for the contest. The prize, of course, was Mary.

The party took place on Sunday afternoon. All the Hunkies came dressed in their best clothes. But none of them compared with Mary Mestrovich. She looked like a queen. She sat on a raised platform. She wore a beautiful red-and-green silk dress bought in the store. Over her head was draped a lace scarf brought from the Old Country by her Slovak grandmother. Her dainty brown fingers sparkled with glass rings.

At the stroke of two, Steve announced the contest. There were to be three rounds. In each round the suitors were to take turns lifting a dolly bar. A dolly bar is a long heavy bar of metal. Anyone who failed to lift the dolly off the ground had to drop out.

The guests cheered their favorites. The young Hunkies rolled up their sleeves. Steve blew the whistle.

One by one the lads bent over the heavy dolly and tugged. The Hunkietown boys raised it easily enough. But one of the Johnstowners and a couple of Homesteaders had to drop out.

'Go sit with the women,' sneered the boastful winners at the unhappy losers.

The second dolly was much heavier than the first. Only three men were able to lift it — Pete Pussick, Eli Stanoski, and a man from Johnstown.

Joe Magarac

These three had still to lift the third dolly, which was much heavier than either of the others.

First the Johnstown fellow tried — in vain. Eli took his place. He pulled and pulled, but for all his straining he couldn't lift the bar. Then came Pete. The crowd cheered and cheered. It was obvious that he was going to be the victor. Mary blushed with pleasure.

Pete puffed and struggled in vain. He managed to get one end of the dolly about an inch off the ground. Try as he might, he couldn't lift it up all at once.

Poor Pete! No prize for him! Poor Mary! No husband for her! And poor Steve! No son-in-law for him, after all his planning and boasting!

Someone in the back of the crowd began to laugh. It wasn't a sneering laugh at all. It sounded like the deep, quiet bubbling of molten steel in the furnaces.

To the astonishment of all, there stood a giant. None of the Hunkies had seen the like of him before. He was seven feet tall if he was an inch. His blue eyes were as clear as a baby's. They twinkled as he grinned at the gaping people. If he hadn't been so large, he would have been a very pleasant-looking fellow.

The crowd parted as he stepped forward. He stooped over the third dolly bar and, with one hand, lifted it over his head and twirled it around as though it were a light cane.

'Hurrah!'

'The winner!'

'He's won!'

Everyone shouted as the big fellow flipped the dolly into the air and caught it behind his back. Steve rushed forward to congratulate him and to find out who he was and where he came from. The giant stood there grinning until the noise

31

died down. Then he told his story. His name was Joe Magarac, he said.

'Joe Magarac!' The Hunkies began to snicker. In the language of the Old Country, 'magarac' means jackass.

'Sure, Magarac, Jackass, that's me,' Joe said. Once again he laughed his deep, bubbling laugh. 'Eat like a mule and work like a mule. That's Magarac.' The Hunkies knew then and there that they were going to love this big fellow, whoever he was.

To their surprise he opened his shirt and invited the men to tap his chest. One by one they cracked their knuckles on his skin and winced with pain. The giant was all steel, not flesh and blood like other men — just hard, cold steel.

He was born in the heart of the iron-ore mountains down in the core of the earth. He had lain there for centuries until a miner stumbled on him and told him about the great world outside. Then he had come down from the hills to work in the steel mills.

While he was telling his tale, Mary sat shuddering. The thought of being married to a steel monster frightened her. When her father explained to the newcomer that he had won himself a wife, she nearly fainted.

But Joe Magarac set her at ease. 'A wife?' he asked. 'What can Magarac do with a wife? Eat like a mule and work like a mule, that's all I want. Let me work in your mill, and let Miss Mestrovich marry Pete, who is the strongest man here except me.'

So Mary and Pete were married with everyone's blessing. Joe was given a job tending open hearth Number Seven in the Hunkietown mill.

What a steel worker he turned out to be! He stayed on the job day and night. He lived, if you could call it that, at the

32

Joe Magarac

Hunkietown boarding-house. The landlady said he was certainly right about his name. He had five meals a day, and at each of them he ate more than any mule she ever saw.

The bosses agreed that he worked like a mule, too! Men came from steel mills all over the country to see him — from Gary and Pittsburgh and Birmingham and Youngstown. It was a pleasure to watch him. He was a whole crew in himself.

First he gathered the raw materials, heavy chunks of ore, pieces of scrap iron, great blocks of limestone, and dumped them into the furnace. Then down on hands and knees, he blew steadily on the fire until it had been fanned to white heat. He didn't bother with the big bellows the ordinary Hunkies used.

When the mass inside had melted down, Joe would sit in the door of Number Seven and with his long steel arm he would stir the mixture round and round and round. Not even the best of the regular workers could stand the fierce blast from the open hearth. But Joe liked it. He sat there stirring for hours without even perspiring.

As soon as the steel had cooked, he poured it into the ingot mould. Then came the part he liked most of all. As the golden mass cooled, Joe grabbed it in his hands as you might take a piece of hot candy at a taffy pull. Handful by handful, he squeezed it between his fingers. Through each slit oozed out a perfect steel rail.

Magarac enjoyed squeezing out rails, eight at a time, so much that soon the mill yard was stacked with them. He was like a baby with a new toy. The foreman suggested that he take a rest now and then. But Joe grinned and shook his head and kept on squeezing. Soon the piles of rails stood so high the mill itself was hidden from view. The company couldn't sell rails as fast as Joe Magarac made them.

The bosses met and sighed over their problem. They decided to close the mill for a week. They didn't like to do it, but there seemed no other way to clear the yard of all Joe's rails.

So the foreman came to Number Seven and told Joe about it. He explained that the fire was to be checked and stoked to burn at low heat. Thus it could be rekindled easily when the mill opened again. The steel giant said nothing, but tears of disappointment gathered in his eyes. He sat down in front of his hearth and shook his head sadly.

The following Monday the mill reopened. The salesmen had been busy. Most of Joe's rails had been sold and shipped away. Only a few small piles were left in the yard. The other firemen poked their fires and fanned their flames. But no one tended Number Seven.

Where was Joe Magarac? They looked high. They looked low. They sent search parties all over Hunkietown. But no trace of the giant could they find.

In the midst of their search, a low bubbly laugh rang out from Joe's old furnace. It grew louder and louder. It sounded as though the furnace was having a good joke all to itself.

The startled Hunkies rushed to Number Seven and looked in. There in the center of a pool of molten steel as golden as sunlight was the grinning head of Joe Magarac. His eyes snapped and twinkled as he called for the foreman and the bosses.

When they came running, Joe explained what he had done. He said he was broken-hearted when the mill shut down. Work like a mule! That was all he knew how to do. And if he couldn't work — well, an empty mill was no place for him!

So, after he stoked his fire, he crawled in on top and melted

34

himself down. All week long as he was cooking, he was thinking. A great thought had come to him.

He asked them to do as he told them. As soon as he was cooked through, they were to mould him into great beams and girders, which would be the purest steel in all the world. Then they were to tear down the old building and around Number Seven they were to build a new one out of these new steel beams. He told them where each rivet was to be placed. This new mill, he said, would be the showplace of the steel industry. There would never be a finer one.

As he finished speaking, his head sank below the surface and all that was left of the great steel giant was the sound of his bubbling laugh.

His instructions were followed to the letter. By spring the new mill was finished. The company declared a holiday and a big party was arranged for the dedication.

As part of the ceremony, they had a contest of strength for the young men. Pete Pussick won. But this time the prize was not Mary Mestrovich. It was the honor of tending open hearth Number Seven in the Joe Magarac mill in Hunkie-town.

The Ghost of Dark Hollow Run

5

MAYBE you don't believe in ghosts. Hans didn't either. But it was a ghost that caused his sad adventure in Dark Hollow Run.

Hans was a poor orphan who lived in Holland almost two hundred years ago. He used to watch the big sailing ships in the harbor at Amsterdam. They came from the English colonies in America. The one thing he wanted more than anything else was to go there.

He had a dream in his head. If only he could get across the ocean, he'd have a fine farm and pretty wife and a family of fat blond children. What more could anybody want? But Hans was poor, too poor to pay for his passage.

One day the captain of a sailing vessel came to him. He said he knew a Dutch farmer in the colony of Penn's Woods. The farmer was rich, but he needed help. If Hans would promise to work for him for seven years, the farmer would pay for his passage to the New World.

Hans almost cried for joy. He signed the papers promising to do anything the farmer asked. Almost before he knew it, he was on the ocean.

On board ship was a pretty Dutch girl named Neltje. Neltje, too, was an orphan. Like Hans she had promised to work for her passage. By the time he reached Philadelphia, Hans was head over heels in love. Of course he was happy when he found out that Neltje was going to work for the wife of his own master. He made up his mind that as soon as their seven years were up, he'd marry Neltje. His dream would come true.

It wasn't long before Hans had learned all about his new job. Farmer Klaus was a kind man, but he worked his servants as hard as he worked himself. Hans had to milk the cows and paint the big red barn and thresh the wheat and carry the water. Although he had been born in the city, he soon knew all the tricks of a big Pennsylvania Dutch farm.

He learned other things, too. The farm servants told him stories about the countryside. One of their favorites was the story of the haunted schoolhouse.

Not far from Farmer Klaus's acres ran a brook which was called Dark Hollow Run. For about a mile it ran through a little ravine, where the trees formed an arch overhead. In the summertime the ravine was very dark.

Here in Dark Hollow stood a crumbled ruin that had once been a village school. Only the walls were standing. Grass grew up where the children used to sit.

Many years before, the farmers had hired a young schoolmaster from Connecticut. He was a stern young man. He sat at his big high desk and scowled at the pupils over the rims of his spectacles. When anything went wrong, he had only one cure. This was a stout birch rod.

He whipped the boys for teasing the girls. He whipped the girls for teasing the boys. He whipped them all for not knowing their lessons. He whipped them for asking too many questions. Sometimes they thought he whipped them to amuse himself.

One warm spring afternoon as the schoolmaster sat scowling at his desk, a bird flew in the open window and perched on his head. He looked so funny that all the children laughed. They giggled and snickered and laughed out loud. They knew the master would be angry. But they just couldn't help it.

They were right, of course. The master was very angry. He picked up his birch rod and whipped all the students. But when he came to the biggest boy, his rod wore out. It had been used so often it broke in half.

This made the schoolmaster more angry than ever.

'Stay in your seats,' he raged. 'I shall cut myself a new rod, and then we'll start at the beginning again. Wicked children! To laugh at your schoolmaster! I see I shall have to beat some sense into your stupid heads.'

With that he strode out the door to the woods to cut himself another birch.

But when he had left, the children left, too. They formed themselves into a double line, led by the biggest boy. They walked out the door and never were seen again.

The schoolmaster returned with his new birch to find an empty schoolhouse. He ran about the county looking for his pupils. The farmers ran after him, blaming him for the disappearance of their sons and daughters.

Of course, no one wanted to use the school building after

that had happened. So a new house was built nearer the village, and the old one fell into disuse. On stormy nights, ever after, the stern schoolmaster returned to walk up and down the Dark Hollow, his birch in his hand, waiting for the children to come back.

But to get back to Hans! When he heard the story he only laughed. Some of his fellow servants believed it. Wild horses couldn't drag them into the ravine on a dark, stormy night. As we said before, however, Hans didn't believe in ghosts.

Neltje heard the story. She was a little frightened. When Hans laughed at her and said he would protect her, she felt better. They often used to walk through the Hollow when their chores were done. Hans would joke about the ghost, and dream about the farm he and Neltje would have some day.

All the farmhands liked Neltje, however. By the time six of his years were over, Hans began to be worried. He had to admit that he had too many rivals.

One morning Farmer Klaus called Hans to him. He had grown very fond of his big Dutch servant. He trusted him completely. He said he was sorry that Hans would soon be leaving him to make his own fortune. As a gift, Farmer Klaus promised to give him fifty acres of good river-bottom land to farm as soon as the year was over.

But since Hans was still his servant he asked him to take the wheat to the mill and to be back by suppertime with the flour.

Hans's hopes and dreams flew sky high! Fifty acres of good black land — all his own! He must tell Neltje of his good fortune. When she heard about it, she would surely

The Ghost of Dark Hollow Run

pay no attention to the other fellows. She would have eyes only for him.

But the mill was a long ride and he had to be off. He had no chance to talk to her before he left. So he stopped only to ask her to meet him in the ravine at sunset.

He set off for the mill with the bags of wheat in front of him. His old mare plodded along happily in spite of his clucking and kicking. Hans whistled and sang. His heart was as light as a feather pillow.

As he rode down the Hollow, he looked lovingly at every stone and every tree. He tried to imagine how Neltje's eyes would shine when he asked her to marry him and share his fifty acres. He tried to picture her sitting beside the school-house in the late afternoon sun, waiting for him.

He laughed as the horse splashed through the water when they forded the brook. By the time he reached the mill his face was as flushed and shiny as an apple.

The miller was a jolly old man. But he was slow. He didn't like to hurry. He liked to sit at his door and smoke his pipe and talk with the farmers who brought corn to be ground. There were several farmers at the mill when Hans arrived. Since he was only a servant, he had to wait his turn.

It seemed to be hours before the miller got around to him. By the time his grist was ground, and the bags of white flour had been sewed up and tied securely to the saddle, the after-noon sun had nearly sunk behind a bank of black clouds.

As the clouds crept higher, Hans grew more nervous. He thought of Neltje waiting beside the schoolhouse. He kicked his heels into the old mare's sides, but Molly wouldn't trot.

Still the sky grew darker and darker. Hans could see the

tops of the trees bending in the distance as the storm moved closer. Finally, just as he reached the ford across the Run and entered Dark Hollow, the storm broke.

The wind whipped through the ravine like a tornado. Poor old Molly, who had refused to trot before, took to her heels and galloped down the road. Hans lost his hat. His long blond hair streamed out behind him.

Then came a flash of lightning and a clap of thunder. It sounded as though it had struck right under Molly's feet. The mare shied and Hans had to throw his arms around her neck to hang on for dear life. The flour bags broke open. Soon Hans and Molly were covered from head to foot with the white powder. Then came the rain.

Meanwhile, Neltje was waiting in the schoolhouse. At first she was only impatient when her beau didn't come on time. Then the black clouds closed in over the Hollow and she became frightened. The old ruin was no place to seek shelter in a storm.

As she sat there shivering, she thought of the schoolmaster and his ghost. She heard the wind z-zinging through the branches. It was only the wind. But to Neltje it sounded like the schoolmaster swinging his birch rod. She heard the first big raindrops falling on the leaves. They were only the raindrops, but to her they sounded like the slow footsteps of the schoolmaster's spirit.

Then came the storm. Neltje sat huddled in a corner, soaking wet, and crying as though her heart would break. She was angry at Hans. She was afraid her mistress would scold her. She was wet and cold and miserable.

And now, above the noise of the storm, she heard something else. A horse's hooves were rushing up the Hollow road. It was Hans, of course!

The Ghost of Dark Hollow Run

She ran to the door of the schoolhouse to meet him. She swore she would forgive him for everything if he would only take her home.

But what did she see? Instead of Hans and lame old Molly, here came a terrible monster. It was galloping toward her like a ghost on horseback. It was white, all white and scary. The awful creature on the horse's back was waving its wild white arms at her.

She couldn't hear what it was yelling. She didn't stop to listen. All she could think of was the ghost of the schoolmaster, riding a horse, and coming to get her.

She took to her heels and ran as fast as she could back to Farmer Klaus's home. Several times she stumbled. She couldn't help looking back. There was the wild white monster riding after her. The faster she ran, the faster it followed and the louder it yelled.

She reached the farmhouse just as the ghost clattered into the barnyard. With a frightened shriek she fell into the kitchen and fainted.

When she came to her senses, Farmer Klaus was laughing. He was laughing so hard his eyes were full of tears. He was holding his sides to keep from splitting.

And on the porch stood Hans, her fellow servant, looking mournfully into the kitchen. His face and clothes were streaked with white flour paste. In his hands he held two empty flour sacks. He was trying to explain that what she had seen was not the schoolmaster's ghost, but him and old Molly.

Farmer Klaus thought the joke so good that he forgave his servant for losing the grist of flour. At the end of the year he kept his promise and made Hans the present of the fifty acres.

But not so Neltje. She didn't think the adventure funny at all. When her year was up she married the village carpenter. And poor Hans spent the rest of his days as a love-sick bachelor on his river-bottom farm.

King Coal

6

'I am a donkey driver,
   The best on the line.
There is no donkey on the road
   That can come up to mine.

'Then shout, boys, hurray,
   My troubles they're but few.
No other donkey on the road
   Can beat Jerusalem Cuckoo.'

SO SANG the mule-drivers, the young boys of fourteen or fifteen who used to work for King Coal. Day after day they worked in the mines. They hauled loads from the min ing chambers to the foot of the shaft. Old King Coal himself was the merry old soul who lived deep in the heart of the Pennsylvania mountains. He was the spirit of anthracite, the hard coal that heats our houses and apartment buildings.

You might expect the mule-boys to be unhappy, living most of their lives underground. As little fellows of eight or nine they were put to work sorting out the good coal from slate and stone. As they grew older they went into the dark shafts to look after the donkeys and later to become full-fledged miners.

Nevertheless, the mule-boys had their fun. They made pets of their donkeys and raced them up and down the mine passages. Or they played tricks on each other and on the grown-up miners. But on Saturday nights they had the best time of all. Then all the people of the mine-patch gathered on the village green for a party. The fiddlers played while the townsfolk danced. The minstrels told their stories and sang their songs, while the boys listened to their tales of the old days in the mines of King Coal.

Many of the stories were about ghosts and fairies who lived in the mines. The miners were superstitious people. They heard the ghostly hammers of the Tommy-knockers. These were strange, gray little gnomes who lived in the tunnels. Of all the weird noises that were heard under the earth, the most familiar was the tap-tap-tapping of these Tommies. Some persons claimed that the noise was made by water seeping through layers of rock and dripping on the floors beneath. But the miners knew this wasn't so. They knew that the Tommy-knockers were going about with their hammers, testing the walls to make sure that all was safe for the humans under their care.

Then there were the ghosts of dead miners who came back to finish their work or to help their fellows. And sometimes the stories had to do with fake ghosts. Once a pair of mule-boys found an old goat. On his horns they fastened a miner's lamp. The poor old beast ran bleating up and down the tunnels in the darkness. He scared the wits out of the miners who saw him and thought he was a spirit. The mule-boys, who were afraid of a thrashing, never told the truth about

their 'spirit,' and for many years the mine was thought to be haunted.

But all the stories the minstrels told were not about the dark life underground. Some of them, like the story of Bachelor John, had to do with the gossip of the mine-patches. Bachelor John was an old peddler. He was truly an ugly old man, with a long scraggly beard and a ragged suit of clothes. On pay-days he came around to sell his shoe-laces and glass jewelry to the miners' wives.

Poor old Bachelor John wanted a wife more than anything in this world. One by one he courted all the widows in the Pennsylvania towns. None of them would marry him. No one would agree to cook his supper and mend his clothes.

One pay-day night Bachelor John stopped at Number Six. He had had a busy day, and at night he curled up in his pack to sleep. The people of the mine-patch, however, gathered at the village tavern for a party. The noise of their dancing and singing made him feel more lonely than ever. At last the keeper of the tavern took pity on the lonesome peddler. He invited him to come to the party and to warm himself at the stove.

As Bachelor John sat on the side-lines watching the fun, a young woman entered the room. She sat down beside him. She was dressed all in black, with a heavy black veil over her face to show that she was a widow. Old John had never seen her before, and soon the thought struck him that she was the only widow in Pennsylvania to whom he had not proposed. Perhaps she would marry him!

He lost no time. Before two dances were over he popped his question. To his amazement the pretty young widow said, 'Yes!' John was so happy he could hardly stand still. He wanted to be married at once. The innkeeper learned of the peddler's good fortune and sent for the squire. The squire came and performed the marriage. The blushing bride kept her veil over her face, but that did not matter to Bachelor John. He was so happy to be married that he danced with every woman at the party. At last, worn out by his joy, he fell asleep on the tavern bench.

In the morning Peddler John awoke. His bride was nowhere to be seen. She had run away.

When the sleepy bridegroom looked for her, all the miners shook their heads. They knew nothing about any wedding, they said. Why! John must have been dreaming! There wasn't any marriage, there wasn't any bride! But as they said this they had to work hard to keep from laughing.

At last the innkeeper told John the joke. The 'bride' had been one of the mule-drivers, dressed up in his sister's clothes. The whole patch had played a trick on the peddler. He wasn't married, after all. Poor old Bachelor John was still Bachelor John!

One of the favorite stories told by the minstrels on the Saturday night sprees was about the Burning Mine. This was a remarkable tale.

Many years before in the Heckscherville Valley a crew of miners had stumbled upon a wonderful cave. Its walls and ceilings were of pure black coal. Unfortunately, however, water had seeped down from springs overhead and in the bitter cold had frozen into icicles. The whole roof of the cave was covered with the green ice. This, of course, made their work harder. They had to chip away the glassy stuff before they could reach the fine coal which they were after.

One of the miners had what he thought was a good idea. He built a fire in the cave on a Saturday afternoon. The heat from the fire would melt the ice, and by Monday, when the

mine opened again, the coal would be free of its covering.
His fellows agreed that this was the thing to do. They put
away their picks and shovels and waited for the fire to do its
work.

When they returned to the mine on Monday they found
that a terrible thing had happened. The heat had indeed
melted the ice. But more than that, it had set fire to the coal.
As soon as the men reached the shaft on Monday morning
they could smell the thick smoke from the huge furnace
underground. This was a terrible disaster.

The mine, of course, was useless. The company closed
down its Heckscherville plant, because no one dared to work
near the awful heat. One by one the miners drifted away
from the patch and went to work in other places. Before
long, the mountain was left to burn by itself.

The vein of coal inside it, however, was so thick that the
fire smoldered on for many years. Under its heat the stone
cracked and broke. Gashes appeared in the sides of the hill
from which poured out thick black smoke. The ground
itself was warm to the touch. The brooks which tumbled
down the hillsides boiled as they ran.

With the coming of winter an even stranger thing happened to the burning mountain. All around it the country
was covered with ice and snow, the trees were bare, and the
grass was brown and dead. But here the grass stayed green,
the trees kept their leaves and blossomed, flowers dotted the
meadows. Any snow that fell from the sky melted and ran
off into the hot-water streams. Birds flying south for the
season saw this summery paradise and settled in its forests,
thinking they had reached South America. It was summer
all year around.

At first the superstitious mining folk were afraid of the

miracle in their midst. To them the whole mountain was bewitched, and although they liked to look at its pleasant greenness from a distance, they refused to go near it.

After some years a brave miner decided that something should be done about the Burning Mine. Underneath the smoldering vein, he knew, ran another vein of coal. It was a shame for this to be wasted. The people who had lived at the Heckscherville patch tried to make him change his mind when they heard about his plans to open up a new shaft. The fairies would surely bring down a curse on the head of anyone who touched the ground, they said.

In spite of their fears he bought the mountain, hired a crew of brave men, and sunk his new shaft. He dug it deep into the earth, far below the one which burned near the surface. Even so, he had trouble. As they chipped out their first passage, the miners ran into a puddle. Its water was so hot it scalded the soles off their boots. They were forced to give up and return to the top to ease their blistered feet.

Marvel of marvels! When they took off their socks they found no marks of the scalding. Instead, all their corns and bunions had been washed away. The skin was perfectly clear and smooth. One of them who had had a scar on his hand had accidentally put his hand in the water. The scar was gone, and instead of the rough, chapped, wrinkled paw of an old man he had the soft smooth hand of a child.

To make sure they weren't dreaming, they ran back to the patch and gathered up all the sick old people. One by one they carried them down into the hot puddle. After a soaking each returned to the surface healthy and young. They had discovered the Fountain of Youth.

When the news got out, all thoughts of coal were forgotten. Who wanted to bother with coal when he heard about the healing waters of the Burning Mine? No one, of course! The new owner changed his plans. Instead of a mine he built a large hotel, with wide porches looking out over the hillside, and pipes running down into the magic well.

In almost no time people began to come from New York and Philadelphia. They came on crutches, on stretchers, and in wheel chairs. After a bath in the healing spring, or a cupful of its water, they danced like children, completely well. Old men who had come to the Burning Mine through the bitter storms of January were soon playing tennis on the hotel courts and dancing in its ballrooms. What a gay place it was!

When the Irish miners saw what was going on, they still shook their heads. No good would come of this, they knew! The fairies would never stand for it.

At last the owner went too far. If the mine water would cure ills in Heckscherville, why wouldn't it do the same everywhere? He put the wonderful water into bottles and kegs and shipped it all over the United States. People who were unable to come to the Mine ordered it by the case. But this time the Irish were right. King Coal himself had been offended.

Suddenly the mine stopped burning. The mountain grew cold, the trees drooped, and the brooks choked with ice. By morning the hotel was covered with icicles and its lovely lawns were knee-deep with snow. Even worse, the Fountain of Youth was gone. No longer did its waters cure the ills of mankind.

The poor hotel-keeper had to give up his new business. Once again the mountain rang with the picks of the miners and the saucy songs of the mule-boys.

Ichabod Paddock

7

IN the old days Nantucket was a noisy, busy place. Weather-beaten sailors with rings in their ears worked on the docks. They climbed the rigging of whaling ships that came into port from the seven seas. Many of them stomped about the town on wooden legs. Their faces and hands were striped with scars. They were a tough lot.

The toughest of them all was old Captain Ichabod Paddock. He had been the master of a whaling ship for as long as anyone on the island could remember. On his ship his word was law. He roared like a lion above the ocean storms.

But once inside the gate of Mrs. Paddock's kitchen garden he was as meek as a lamb. He couldn't call his soul his own. Frail little Mrs. Paddock had him under her thumb. It was, 'Ichabod, wear your boots.' It was, 'Ichabod, don't trail dirt into the parlor.' It was, 'Ichabod, do this; Ichabod, do that,' from morning until night.

Now, Ichabod loved his wife. He brought her presents from whaling stations all over the world. He brought her rugs from Persia, porcelain from China, and ivory from Africa. But as you can see, he didn't have much fun at home.

Some of the islanders said that was why he spent so much time chasing Crooked Jaw. Crooked Jaw was a mean old whale who was known from Hong Kong to Halifax. They had all tried to get him. But none had ever sunk a harpoon into his tough old hide.

A prize was offered to the whaler who could bring him in. Ichabod heard about it one morning as he was doing an errand for his bossy wife. Right away he straightened his shoulders and wiped the hen-pecked look off his face. 'Here's my chance,' he said. So he jumped over the garden fence, picked up his sea chest, kissed Mrs. P. good-bye, and ran to the harbor.

He lost no time fitting out his ship. He rounded up the biggest, strongest, meanest crew on the island. The sail-makers mended the sails. The blacksmiths sharpened the harpoons and the lances. The merchants filled the hold with supplies for a ten-year cruise. By the first running of the tide the sturdy little whaling ship was ready to ride out of the cove.

When he felt the swell of the ocean under him, Ichabod made a solemn vow. He wouldn't come back to Nantucket until he had Crooked Jaw's oil in his barrels.

It was a year before he and his crew caught up with the big old whale. They were dodging icebergs off the coast of Greenland when the lookout yelled, 'Thar she blows!'

Sure enough! Off to the north they saw a little white feather of steam. It had a funny twist in the middle that meant only one thing. Crooked Jaw! They lowered the boat. Captain Ichabod himself took the harpoon and stood in the bow. The men pulled on their oars for all they were worth. Soon they were almost on top of their prize.

Crooked Jaw was an ugly beast. He had a hump on his back. His big lopsided head looked like a cliff rising out of the water. The flukes of his tail were as wide as the whale-boat was long. His little pig eyes glared red as he caught sight of the captain. Even Ichabod, the master whaler, felt his knees shake as he came face to face with his sworn enemy.

With a powerful thrust he threw the harpoon at the hump on the whale's back. It struck the leathery hide and slid off into the water without catching hold. Crooked Jaw winked his little red eye as much as to say, 'Thought you had me, didn't you?' With a flip of his flukes that sent Ichabod sprawling flat on his back, the whale dove to the bottom of the sea.

The next year they caught up with him near Australia. Meanwhile Captain Ichabod had made himself a new harpoon, twice as heavy and twice as sharp as the first. He spent five hours a day practicing with it to be ready for his enemy.

But this time the same thing happened. Crooked Jaw shrugged his skin, winked his eye, and dove to the bottom, unscratched.

Once a year for the following eight years the captain and the whale exchanged courtesies. The more they met, the madder Ichabod became. Every year he made himself a new harpoon. The last two or three were so heavy that he could hardly lift them. He practiced until the muscles of his right arm were too big for his coat-sleeve. And still he couldn't pierce Crooked Jaw's hide.

The last time they met, Ichabod lost his temper. 'I'll fix

that whale,' he muttered to himself. 'If iron won't get him from the outside, it'll get him from the inside.'

So he tucked a dagger in his belt before he took his stand at the bow of the whaleboat. He lifted the harpoon as if he were going to strike. This time he didn't throw it. To Crooked Jaw's surprise he simply dropped it overboard and jumped in after it. As the giant beast opened his mouth in amazement, Captain Ichabod swam down his throat.

Such a coughing and spluttering as took place then has never been heard or seen since! The brave captain was tossed this way and that. He was shaken up and shaken down. He felt himself being sucked through a whirlpool into the whale's stomach. He grabbed right and left to find something to hang onto. Before he could right himself he was dumped, 'bang,' onto a hard rocky floor.

He lay there awhile, too worn out to move. At first he could see nothing. But as his eyes grew accustomed to the blackness he saw a little light flickering in the distance. He rubbed his bruises and dragged himself toward it.

You can imagine his surprise when he reached the place it came from. There was a stout oaken door with a shiny brass knocker. Over the door hung a trim little lantern. In front of the stoop lay a mat with 'Welcome' written on it.

He didn't really believe what he saw. But he lifted the knocker and let it fall. It rang with a sweet note. From inside the door came a lovely woman's voice, 'Come in, Captain Paddock.'

Ichabod's hair stood straight up on end. His teeth chattered. His knees knocked together like shutters in a high wind.

Because he couldn't help himself, he lifted the knocker again and let it fall. This time it rang with a heavy iron

clang. A deep bass voice called: 'Come right in, Paddock. We've been waiting for you for ten years.'

At that, the captain opened the door. There, in as pretty a ship's cabin as any he'd ever seen on a Yankee clipper, sat two people playing cards. One was a beautiful mermaid with eyes as green as seaweed and hair as red as the sunset. The other was a cross-looking man in a red suit, with crooked horns and a long red forked tail. Ichabod knew well enough who this was — none but the Devil himself.

The mermaid smiled and asked him to sit down. 'We'll be through in a minute,' she explained.

'You see, we're in the middle of a game of rummy. We're playing for a valuable prize.'

'Wh-wh-what is the prize?' stammered the whaler, trying to be polite.

The Devil scowled. He lifted his tail and pointed its fork at Ichabod. 'You!' he snarled.

'And stop that racket,' he added, as Captain Paddock's teeth began to chatter like castanets.

The game was soon over. After a couple of plays the lovely mermaid laid down her last card and said, 'Rummy!' She had won.

The Devil screamed with anger. 'You've tricked me!' he shrieked. 'You've tricked me! But I'll get the best of you yet.' With a flash of sulphur and brimstone he disappeared.

The next thing Ichabod knew he was lying on the floor. The mermaid was holding a bottle of smelling salts under his nose.

'I'm sorry he frightened you,' she was saying. 'He can be very rude sometimes. I hope you'll forgive us.' With that she placed a hand under his shoulders and helped the captain sit up. The smell of sulphur was gone and in its place was another smell, warm and delicious. It made his mouth water.

As he sat up blinking he saw that the table on which the cards had been spread was set for dinner. At each of the two places was a steaming bowl of good New England clam chowder. Beside it was a plate of johnnycake, and from the little cookstove oven came still more delightful odors.

'You must be very hungry after all you've been through,' said the mermaid in her soothing voice. 'Do join me in a simple little supper.'

Now, you must remember that the captain had been at sea for ten years. For breakfast, dinner, and supper, dried beef and hardtack were all he had had to eat. No man in his shoes could resist her invitation.

After the chowder came roast turkey with stuffing and baked squash and pumpkin pie and gingerbread and all the good things he'd remembered from his days on land.

When the mermaid finally cleared the table, Ichabod, who was feeling much better by this time, pulled out his pipe and began to tell stories about his adventures. He was so happy smoking his pipe and bragging to his pretty new friend that he forgot all about his plan to kill the whale.

When it was time for him to stop bragging and return to his ship, he bowed his most courtly bow and promised to come back for supper on Tuesday.

His men didn't know what to make of it. They thought he was dead. They were kneeling on the deck, saying prayers for his departed soul, when he climbed over the railing soaking wet. Of course, they were glad to see him alive. But from the strange gleam in his eye they knew he was bewitched. They tried once or twice to ask what had happened. But after he had beaten up the first mate and the cook, they went about their business with no more questions. Bewitched or not, Captain Paddock was still the toughest skipper in the whale trade.

Crooked Jaw, their former enemy, no longer tried to avoid them. The big whale had had a change of heart. He romped and played in front of the ship like a St. Bernard puppy. And everywhere he went, Ichabod followed. The pilot was ordered never to let the whale out of his sight.

It was a good thing, too. Crooked Jaw led them from one school of fish to another. Before long the hold was chuck full of whale oil. The deck was piled high with whalebone. Every man on board knew that he'd be rich when he got back to Nantucket.

The only thing that worried the crew was their poor bewitched captain. Every Tuesday and every Friday he spent the day in his cabin. He polished his boots. He brushed his best Sunday uniform. He starched his lace cuffs. He combed his beard and waxed his mustache. At suppertime, in all his finery, he jumped overboard and swam boldly into Crooked Jaw's open mouth.

Strange to tell, Captain Paddock got fatter and fatter. His men, after ten years of hardtack and dried beef, were growing thinner and thinner. One Friday night, after the skipper had come back to his ship, the cabin boy hung up his clothes to dry. He noticed something sticky in one of the coat pockets. When he put in his hand he pulled out a soaking blob of what smelled and tasted like gingerbread.

The captain had forgotten all about his wife. He'd forgotten all about his solemn vow. And worst of all, he'd forgotten about his first meeting with the mermaid and about the Devil's part in the picture. So it never occurred to him as he followed Crooked Jaw over the ocean and enjoyed his

Ichabod Paddock

pleasant Tuesday and Friday suppers, that he was being led into trouble.

He didn't pay any attention to directions. He didn't see that the Devil was leading the whale. And he didn't see that the whale was leading him back to Nantucket. He was too bewitched to see that he'd sailed right up in front of Mrs. Paddock's kitchen garden.

Mrs. Paddock was in her garden. She was overjoyed to see her husband's ship sail into view. She ran into the house for her spy-glass. When she looked through it, she saw her husband standing on the deck, fat and healthy and dressed up in his Sunday best.

Then she saw something that changed her joy to sorrow. The captain jumped overboard and swam right into the jaws of a giant whale. She cried aloud as though her heart would break.

The men on the ship heard her cries. When they recognized the village of Nantucket in the distance, they didn't know what to do. They couldn't go ashore without the skipper. And he was in the middle of the whale.

They held a meeting on the deck. After a long discussion they decided to send the cabin boy ashore to tell the captain's wife about his tragedy. Maybe she would be able to help them all.

When she first heard the story she sobbed louder than ever. Her neighbors came to comfort her. They began to sob. The poor little cabin boy howled along with the rest of them. The racket made Crooked Jaw lift his head out of the water.

As he did so, Mrs. Paddock looked up. Being a clever woman, she saw at once that there was a witch inside the whale. She knew what to do about that.

She wiped her eyes and sent her neighbors home. She built

a big fire in the stove. She collected all her silver, her great-aunt's tea set, her grandmother's spoons, and her own best thimble. She put them in a kettle and melted them down. From the melted silver she made a fine little harpoon, just big enough to fit her frail hand.

When the skipper climbed over the railing that night, shaking the water out of his eyes and licking the last crumb of gingerbread off his mustache, there stood his loving wife.

She wasted no time for foolishness. 'Ichabod,' she said, holding her silver harpoon in one hand and grabbing her husband's ear in the other, 'you and I are going whaling.' With that she marched him off to the smallest whaleboat. The men lowered the boat into the water.

'Now, Ichabod, start rowing,' ordered Mrs. Paddock as she took her place in the bow and lifted her silver harpoon.

As soon as Crooked Jaw saw her coming, he had the fright of his life. The old whale knew only too well that silver will always kill a witch. And, of course, a mermaid is a witch of the sea. He tried to dive to the bottom. But Mrs. P. was too quick for him. The harpoon held fast. The terrified whale dashed back and forth, carrying the captain and his wife on the wildest Nantucket sleigh-ride of all time.

When at last the monster was worn out and brought in to the harbor, the captain tried to tell his strange story. Most of the townsfolk raised their eyebrows and tapped their foreheads. They thought he was touched. Mrs. Paddock said simply, 'Ichabod, don't talk such nonsense.'

But when Crooked Jaw was cut up for oil, inside his stomach was found a long piece of seaweed shaped something like a mermaid. And where her hair should have been, the weed was as red as the sunset.

Stormalong

8

Stormy's gone, that good old man,
To my way, hay, storm along, John!
Stormy's gone, that good old man,
To my aye, aye, aye, Mister Stormalong.'

STORMY'S gone, of course. He died before the last
Yankee clipper furled her silver sails. But stories about
'that good old man' are told still wherever old sailors
gather. Just where Old Stormalong was born isn't important. He first appeared on a wharf in Boston Harbor. The
captain of the *Lady of the Sea*, the largest clipper ship in the
China trade, was signing on men. Stormy gave his full name,
Alfred Bullrod Stormalong. Without looking up from his
ledger, the captain wrote down the initials, 'A. B.'

A. B. Stormalong stood five fathoms tall, which is the
same as thirty feet. The captain glanced up at his new man.
He whistled with surprise. 'Phew!' he said. 'There's an
able-bodied seaman for you, boys.'

Someone noticed that the giant's initials stood for just

that. From that day to this sailors have tacked A. B. after their names. This shows that they are able-bodied seamen like Stormy.

Old Stormalong's size and strength helped him a lot on the sea. He didn't have to climb the rigging to furl the topsails. He just reached up from the deck and did it. He could hold the pilot's wheel with his little finger even in the worst weather. In less than a week he'd been promoted from common sailor to bos'n.

The cook didn't care much for his company, however. He made too much work in the galley. He had a weakness for food. He knew a good deal about cooking and wanted everything prepared just so. Besides, he wanted lots of it.

He liked a couple of ostrich eggs fried sunny-side-up for breakfast. For lunch he expected a dory full of soup. After his meals he used to lie out on deck in the sun and pick his teeth with an oar.

But Old Stormy was too valuable a man to dismiss because of the cook's grumbling. There were many occasions on which the *Lady of the Sea* would have become the *Lady on the Bottom of the Sea*, had it not been for her bos'n.

Once, for instance, in the warm waters of the tropical Atlantic, the captain gave orders to hoist sail and weigh anchor after a morning of deep-sea fishing. The crew heaved and strained at the capstan bars. The anchor refused to budge. Something was holding it fast to the bottom. Not even when Stormalong heaved along with the crew would the heavy iron stir.

So Old Stormy stuck a knife into his belt and dove overboard to have a 'look-see.' Hand over hand he climbed down the anchor chain. Suddenly great waves arose. A commotion began on the ocean floor. The surface frothed and

64

churned. From below came sounds of battle. The crew could see dimly two dark forms struggling in the water's depths. Then the long, black, slimy arm of a giant octopus slapped into the air.

At the sight of it the crew gave up their bos'n for lost. No human being could possibly fight single-handed one of those great devils of the sea and come out alive. But before they had a chance to arrange a funeral service for him, Old Stormalong climbed slowly up the chain and pulled himself on deck.

'Phew!' he sighed. 'That old squid was a tough one. Had hold of the anchor with fifty arms and grabbed the bottom with the other fifty. He won't trouble us now, though. Tied him tighter than a schoolboy's shoe-lace. Tied every one of his arms in a double knot.'

A year or so after this adventure Old Stormy lost his taste for the sailor's life. He said it was the food. He was tired of hardtack and dried fish. He had a hankering for some tender, fresh green vegetables.

His shipmates, however, guessed that the real trouble was lack of space. The *Lady of the Sea* was the biggest clipper afloat, but even so she cramped her bos'n. He couldn't sleep stretched out anywhere on board.

After a last voyage around Cape Horn, Stormalong left the wharf at Boston with his pay in his pocket and an eighteen-foot oar over his shoulder. He bade his friends good-bye. He said he was going to walk west, due west. He would stop and settle down as soon as someone asked what the long pole might be. He figured that any county whose inhabitants didn't recognize an oar was far enough from the coast for him.

The *Lady's* crew heard nothing from their shipmate for several years. Then in the San Francisco gold rush the mate had news. Stormy had bought a township and was one of

66

the best farmers in the whole U.S.A. Stormy a farmer? The mate couldn't believe his ears. But when he was told of Farmer Stormalong's miracles, he knew it was his man, without a doubt!

Stormalong specialized in potatoes. During his first growing season the whole countryside dried up. It didn't rain for six weeks. The little spring that fed the horse trough gave only enough water for the stock. There was not an extra drop with which to irrigate the crops.

Then Old Stormalong went to work. He labored over those drooping, dying plants until the perspiration ran from him in rivers. He sprinkled those potatoes with the sweat of his brow. At the end of the season, when other farmers were moaning over their burnt acres, he drove to market with a bumper crop of the largest, tastiest spuds ever to be mashed with cream and butter.

In spite of this success, Stormy wearied of farm life. He was a restless fellow. Often at night when he had milked the cows and locked the hen roost, he sat in front of his stove and dreamed about the old days on the ocean. At last he couldn't deny to himself that the sea was calling him back.

Word spread through the countryside about a new ship, the *Courser*. It was so huge that it couldn't enter Boston Harbor. The inlanders thought it was just another Yankee yarn. They laughed about it as they sat on the front porch of the country store. But to Stormalong the *Courser* was more than a fable. It was a dream come true.

He sold his farm and returned to the East. For several days he hung around the waterfront, looking like the ghost of his former self. His ruddy salt-sea color was gone, his eyes had lost their shine, and the 'shellbacks,' or sailors, who had known him in the old days realized that he was a sick man, yearning for the feel of the spray.

They couldn't tell him much about the whereabouts of the big ship he was seeking. It was a real boat, all right. It had anchored outside of Cape Cod some time before with a cargo of elephants for Mr. Barnum's circus. The *Lady of the Sea* had been pressed into service as a tender to bring the freight to shore.

The more the old bos'n heard about the *Courser* the more his mouth watered to see her and join her crew. At last, when a whaler brought word that she was cruising along the Grand Banks off Nova Scotia, Stormy couldn't stand it any longer. He dove off T Wharf and swam out to sea.

The next time his old friends saw him, he was the captain of the big vessel. The old fire was back in his eyes, his cheeks were brown as mahogany, and his spirit was dancing. For the *Courser* was the only ship in all the world which suited him. He was the only skipper in all the world to do her justice.

She was so long from stem to stern that it took a man on horseback a good twenty-four hours to make the trip. A string of Arab ponies were stabled in front of the fore-bitts for the use of the officers on duty. The masts were hinged to let the sun and moon go by. The mainsail had been cut and hemmed in the Sahara Desert, the only expanse of land large enough for the operation. When a storm blew up from the horizon, the skipper had to give the order to man the topsails a good week in advance. It took the men that long to climb the rigging.

This last fact had its disadvantages, of course. Until the United States Weather Bureau caught on to the trick of sending out weather reports in advance, the *Courser* was often

Stormalong

caught in a hurricane without notice enough to furl in her cloth. She was large enough to ride out any storm, even in full sail, without much damage. But there was no way of telling how far off her course she'd be blown in the process.

One time, for instance, during a North Atlantic winter gale, the *Courser* was pushed this way and that until she ended up in the North Sea. As you know, the North Sea is just a little sea, and not in the same class with an honest-to-goodness ocean. In fact, it was so small and crowded with islands that the *Courser* couldn't turn around.

There to port lay Norway and Denmark. Straight ahead lay the continent of Europe, and to starboard the British Isles. Stormy roared with anguish. He feared lest his clipper, his lovely queen of the five oceans, would have to join the lowly North Sea fishing fleet for the rest of time.

There was a way out, however. When Stormalong and the mate measured the English Channel they found that at high tide it was an inch or two wider than the *Courser*. With luck they might squeeze through it and out into the Atlantic again.

So the skipper sent the officers to Holland to buy up all the soap in sight. Then he put his crew to work, soaping the sides of the big boat. They slapped the greasy stuff on thick until the *Courser* was as slippery as an eel.

Captain A. B. Stormalong himself took the pilot's wheel and steered. Just at the turn of tide, with her full sails set, the *Courser* glided through into the broad Atlantic Ocean. But she had a close call. The headlands on the English coast scraped most of the soap off the starboard side of the vessel. To this day the cliffs at Dover have been white.

After this adventure Old Stormy was talked about in every port in the world. No sailor could deny that his highest

69

ambition was to ship on the *Courser* under 'that good old man.'

Great was the mourning from Portsmouth to Hongkong when news of Stormalong's death finally came. Several reports of it were spread around. One version had it that he was drowned in a storm off Cape Hope. But most of the tales agreed that he died of indigestion. His magnificent appetite had finished him.

His old shipmates gathered for the funeral. They made him a shroud of the finest China silk. They dug his grave with a silver spade. They lowered his coffin into the ground with a silver chain, the color of his sails. And the tears that fell from the eyes of those hard old salts drenched the earth like the rain of a nor'easter.

> 'Old Stormy has heard an angel call,
> To my way, hay, storm along, John.
> So sing his dirge now, one and all,
> To my aye, aye, aye, Mister Stormalong.'

The South

Ole Massa and His Chillun

9

I. THE FLOOD

UNLIKE the other chapters of this book, this tells three stories, not one. These tales are very, very old, so old that no one knows where they came from. The negro slaves told them in the cotton fields of Georgia and Alabama, in the tobacco fields of the Carolinas, and in the rice fields of Louisiana. Some persons think they were brought from Africa when the negroes were taken from their homes to serve the colonial planters. Others think that they were first told by the Indians.

In the very beginning of the world, before man was created, the animals were the important creatures. They carried on all the business and ran the government, as human beings do today. The lion was their king. Every year they met in a big assembly to talk things over.

One year the assembly met as usual. The elephants, the giraffes, the zebras, the dogs, the cats, the hummingbirds, the pigeons, the dragonflies, the spiders, the lobsters, the crawfish, the earthworms — they all packed up their lunches, put on their Sunday clothes, and went to the meeting.

Mr. Lion sat upon his throne and tried to call the crowd to order. He had a hard time of it. Everyone wanted to talk at once. The mule brayed and the cow mooed and the pig squealed. The tiger growled and the coyote howled and the panther snarled. Every one of the big important animals made a speech. The confusion, of course, was awful. No one could hear himself think.

The elephant became excited. He stomped up and down trying to make himself heard. Without knowing it, he trampled on one of the crawfish and smashed him into the mud. That was the end of Mr. Crawfish.

The other crawfish were worried. They were little creatures and certainly no match for the elephant. While they were worrying, the big beast put his foot down again. Squash! Another crawfish was ground into the mud!

This made the tiny animals angry. They gathered together all their cousins and uncles and aunts and went to King Lion. They drew up a long speech, complaining about the elephant's carelessness. But with all the noise going on, King Lion couldn't hear them. He paid them no attention at all.

The crawfish ran up and down through the crowd, trying to find someone who would listen to their complaint. The mule kept on braying, the cow kept on mooing, and the pig kept right on squealing. Only the mud turtle and the spring lizard would pay them any attention.

At last they lost their patience. They were so frightened and so angry they decided to quit the assembly, for good and all. With their friends, the turtle and the lizard, they took the shortest way out. They bored holes into the ground and disappeared. Down, down, down they bored until they reached the springs under the earth. They were at last safe from the elephant's clumsy feet.

But what about the other animals? When the crawfish hit the hidden springs, water began to spout up from their holes. It gushed up and up until it covered the whole world with a great flood. All the other animals, who were too busy and too big and too important to look out for their small friends, were carried away by the waters and drowned.

II. WHY THE NEGRO WORKS SO HARD

Up in the sky above the troubles of the earth sat Ole Massa. He was a kindly old man with a white beard and a black frock coat, who looked after his 'chillun' down below. When the waters of the flood had gone down, he took the world away from the animals and gave it to men.

At first all men were alike. Large and small, weak and strong, white and black, they lived together as brothers. None of them had to work. Ole Massa gave them pork chops to eat and store clothes to wear. It was a happy time, indeed.

At last Ole Massa saw that man was becoming very lazy. His 'chillun' expected him to do all the work. All they wanted to do was to lie out under the trees and sing and laugh and eat fruit. He decided that something would have to be done about this sad state of affairs.

One day he sent down two bundles tied up with fancy ribbons. One was a big bundle with curious bumps and bulges that looked interesting. The other was a little one, a poor thing at best. Ole Massa himself came down and made an announcement.

These two bundles were prizes, he said. All the men in the world were to run a footrace. The winner of the race should have the big prize, the loser the little one. This aroused his lazy 'chillun.' Each of them wanted to win the big, bumpy parcel.

At last the day of the race dawned. Ole Massa sat in the judges' stand, very handsome in his silk hat and his black coat. The women and children cheered from the side. The men danced up and down at the starting point. Then they were off!

At first the white man ran ahead, but before the race was over, the black man was in the lead. His long legs carried him to the victory. The white man was left far behind, gasping for breath.

Proudly the winner stepped up to the stand to receive his prize. Behind him stood the unhappy loser. Ole Massa brought out the two bundles. Before he presented them, he made a speech.

'Oh, my chillun,' he said, 'for a long time you have been lazy and good-for-nothing. Now you must work. Each of these prizes contains tools. Take them and use them!'

With that he wrapped himself up in a cloud and vanished.

The white man opened his prize first. There lay a pen and a bottle of ink. He knew well enough what to do with them. Without any further ado he pulled down a big piece of paper and began to write. He wrote figures, accounts, letters, stories, books, orders, laws, and anything that could be written with pen and ink.

Then the black man opened his big prize. He wept when he saw what it contained. Inside lay a plow and a hoe and a sickle and a pick and a shovel and an axe. These were the tools of the hard work. He knew well enough what to do with them.

Ever since that day the white man has been figuring with

his pen, sitting in an office in his store clothes; and the negro
has been bending his back and straining his muscles, hoeing
the corn and chopping the wood and picking the cotton and
plowing the field.

This is why, said the slaves, the negro has to work so
hard.

III. BRER RABBIT AND THE TAR BABY

The hero of most of the old negro stories was neither a
giant nor a wise man. He was Brer Rabbit, as sly and mischievous a creature as has ever been seen. He spent his time
playing tricks on the other animals, especially on Brer Fox.

Time after time Brer Fox thought he had Brer Rabbit under
his thumb. He licked his chops and filled his kettle, expecting to dine off rabbit. But time after time the cottontail
made a fool out of the greedy fox.

The most famous of his pranks concerns the tar baby. The
fox was tired of being tricked by his long-eared friend. His
mouth watered for a steaming plate of stew, rabbit stew.
What's more, he thought he knew how he could solve both
problems at once.

Brer Fox fancied himself an artist. Some careless person
had left a bucket of tar about, and this was exactly what he
wanted. With great pains he went to work and modeled a
little man from the sticky black stuff. It was a fine statue,
life-sized and for all the world like a pickaninny. On its
head Master Fox placed an old straw hat. It certainly looked
real.

With this manikin he planned to catch his old enemy. He
placed the little tar fellow beside the road and hid himself in
the bushes to see the fun.

Soon, clippety-clop, down the road came Brer Rabbit.

Ole Massa and His Chillun

Being a friendly soul, Master Rabbit stopped to say 'Howdy!' to the little black stranger. The tar baby, of course, said nothing.

'Good morning,' said the rabbit, a little louder, and he tipped his hat. The tar baby said nothing at all.

This seemed rude to Brer Rabbit. All the animals, even the fox and the wolf, said 'Howdy' to one another.

Brer Rabbit walked up closer and yelled, 'Nice weather we're having' at the black figure. Still the tar baby said nothing.

'Well,' snorted the rabbit, 'you're stuck-up, aren't you? Don't you know enough to speak when you're spoken to? If you don't, I'll slap your sassy face.'

The tar baby, of course, said nothing. The rabbit was as good as his word. He slapped the black creature with his right paw. This was what the fox had planned all along. The paw stuck fast in the sticky tar.

Brer Rabbit was becoming angry. 'Let me go!' he raged. 'You're not only stuck-up, you're mean. If you don't let me go I'll slap you with my other hand.'

When the tar baby paid no attention to his raving, Brer Rabbit reached out and slapped him again with his left paw. It stuck, too. The fox, hiding in the underbrush, had to hold his sides to keep from laughing out loud.

Then the rabbit began to kick. First he kicked with his right foot, which stuck fast in the tar, then with his left. He was furious.

'If you don't let me go,' he yelled, 'I'll butt you with my head, you low-down, mean, stuck-up thing, you!' The tar baby sat as still as a lump on a log, and Brer Rabbit butted. Here he was, completely stuck up in the ball of tar! He couldn't budge.

The fox came out from his hiding place with tears of laughter falling down his cheeks. His little joke had worked perfectly. No more would he have to suffer the insults of the saucy cottontail. He and Mrs. Fox and all the little foxes would have themselves a feast.

Immediately Brer Rabbit saw that he had fallen into a trap. For all his slyness, he had been caught. But he didn't turn a hair when he saw Mr. Fox. His mind began to work faster than it had ever worked before. He had to get himself out of the pickle he was in.

Turning to his captor he put on his saddest expression. Crocodile tears came to his eyes. 'You've finally caught me, Mr. Fox,' he sniffed. 'Yes, I know I've been mean to you in my day and I deserve anything and everything you will do to me... (sniff!)... I'm sorry for all the trouble I've caused you. Really, I am, dear Mr. Fox... (sniff!)... I've been a selfish, mischievous, horrid rabbit... Do with me what you like.'

Brer Fox was pleased with himself. He let the rabbit go on with his humble apologies.

'Do anything you wish, dear Mr. Fox,' sobbed Brer Rabbit, looking up quickly to see how his enemy was taking his talk, 'anything at all... but please, kind Mr. Fox, don't throw me in the briar patch. Roast me alive! I deserve that.'

The fox scratched his head. 'It's too much trouble to build a fire,' he said. 'I think I'll hang you instead.'

'Oh, hang me, please, hang me,' begged the rabbit, looking very humble. 'Hang me from the highest tree in the forest. But don't throw me in the briar patch.'

'I haven't any string,' said the fox. 'I'll have to drown you.'

'Drown me, then,' murmured the rabbit, pretending to be

faint with fear. 'I don't care any more. Drown me, if you wish, but please, oh, please, *don't* throw me in the *briar patch*.'

This time Brer Fox lost his head. He said to himself: 'If he's so afraid of the briar patch, that's the very thing. I'll throw him in right away.'

Without any more conversation, the fox picked up the rabbit by the leg. He swung him around his head and threw him as hard as he could into the middle of the briar bushes. This, of course, was exactly what Brer Rabbit wanted him to do. The thorns scratched the tar from his hands and feet and head. In a flash he had scrambled free and was off up the hill.

The next thing Brer Fox knew, his rabbit stew was sitting at the top of the hill as saucily as ever. He had been fooled again!

'I was born and bred in a briar patch,' sang the rabbit mischievously, as he disappeared over the hilltop, 'born and bred in a briar patch.'

Mule Humans

10

THE mountain people of Kentucky are very careful of their speech on Amber Days. These are the days which Old Horny, the Devil, has planted among the others in the calendar in order to trap weak humans. If anyone makes a false wish on one of these days, it will come true. You may laugh and say this is just a foolish superstition, but the Kentucky people know better. They saw what happened to Godsey Scrorse and his wife Mondie.

Mr. and Mrs. Scrorse lived in a tumble-down cabin halfway up the mountain. They had an old sow and some little pigs, a few chickens, and a patch of corn. Godsey was a clumsy, lazy old fellow who spent most of his time just 'a-settin'.' And Mondie was as impatient and as cross as her man was lazy.

One afternoon, as Mondie was sweeping the cabin floor, Godsey kept getting in her way. He lay sprawled out just where she wanted to sweep. When he moved, he tripped over the broom. Mondie began to scold. Godsey scolded back. Soon they were quarreling, yelling, and calling names at each other, like a pair of jay-birds.

'You're a fine one,' Mondie stormed. 'Always in the way. Clumping on everyone's feet. Just like a mule. The fact is, you're nothing but a mule from the waist down.'

'Oh, stop your chattering,' Godsey retorted. 'You're always braying at people. In fact, you're nothing but a mule from the neck up.'

'Is that so?' Mondie tried to say. Instead of the words, however, all that came out was the high, shrill bray of a donkey, 'Eee-yaw!'

Poor Godsey! He looked at his wife and saw that her head had suddenly turned into the long bony head of a mule. He was so frightened he jumped up and tried to run out of the cabin door.

His own head hit the ceiling. He looked down. Instead of his two legs, he had the four long legs of a jackass.

They stared at each other with horror. Then they saw the calendar. It was an Amber Day!

Mondie began to sob, 'We're bewitched!' But not a word came out, nothing but 'Eee-yaw! Eee-yaw!' Godsey tried to put his arms around her to comfort her, but his four long legs were hard to manage. One of his heavy, horny hoofs came down 'plunk' on her foot! She brayed louder than ever

At last Godsey decided to ask Solomon Shell what to do. Solomon was a wise man, a story-teller, who lived in the valley. He was a famous old fellow, with long hair hanging over his shoulders, and a beard 'as wild as a stubble-patch.' His neighbors believed he was a devil-charmer. If anyone knew how to cure an Amber Day enchantment, Solomon Shell certainly did.

So Godsey left Mondie rocking sadly by the fire, with her

big donkey head in her hands. He scrunched himself through the low doorway and galloped down the valley road.

Old Solomon was surprised to see his friend peering in at him through the top of the window. He thought Godsey must be standing on a chair.

'Come in, neighbor Scrorse,' he called. 'Sit down by the fire.'

Godsey shook his head. 'Can't come in,' he answered sadly. 'Can't sit down, either.'

'What's the matter, Godsey?'

'You'll have to come and see for yourself,' was the mournful reply.

So Solomon knocked out his pipe and went to his door. There, of course, was Godsey, with his long mule legs. He wasn't standing on any chair, after all. His empty trousers flapped in front of his powerful forelegs.

'Whew!' whistled the wise man in astonishment. At his whistle, the mule's hind legs began to prance and his tail switched.

'Whoa, boy! Whoa, Godsey!' called the unhappy Mr. Scrorse to his donkey half. Then he explained what had happened. He told the old story-teller how he and Mondie had quarreled, how they had forgotten about Amber Day, and how they had been changed into Mule Humans. He had come to ask Solomon to help them.

'Well,' said the wise fellow, stroking his wild beard, 'I don't know exactly what I can do for you. Amber Day poison is mighty strong poison. It's hard to cure.'

Godsey's hopes began to fade as Old Sol shook his head. He could make only one suggestion himself.

'I thought you could take the mule out of us and swap your shoats for it. It's a powerful beast,' he said. He whacked himself on the haunch to show Solomon how sturdy the donkey was.

'Yes,' agreed Solomon, 'maybe I could at that. But before I swap my pigs for any four-legged beast, I want to have a look at the whole beast.'

'Climb up!' cried Godsey, pointing to the mule's back. 'Climb up and come have a look at Mondie.'

So Solomon pulled himself up on Godsey's donkey-back. He took one of the empty trouser-legs in each hand as reins. He dug his heels into the creature's sides. The hind legs danced and bounced for a moment.

'Gee-up!' yelled Godsey. And off they went!

What a ride they had! Old Sol declared later he expected to be shaken plumb to pieces. The closer they got to the Scrorse cabin, the more anxious Godsey became to have the enchantment cured. The faster he galloped.

A mule's back is not the most comfortable seat in the world. And Godsey had got himself changed into one of the toughest, boniest critters that ever lived. His backbone stuck up like the ridgepole of a barn. It wasn't long before Solomon had to let go of the trousers and clasp his arms around Godsey's waist in order to hang on.

They raced up the valley road, whooping and hollering, scaring pigs and chickens out of their path. Solomon hung on for dear life. His long hair and his scraggly beard flapped behind him like clothes on a washline. The sweat poured down Godsey's neck and off his flanks. His tongue hung out.

On the way they passed Preacher Charlie's cabin. Preacher Charlie was just returning from the well with a bucket of cold water in each hand.

Godsey paused to ask him for a drink. But when Preacher Charlie saw him, his hair stood up on end.

88

Mule Humans

'Heavens above us!' he shrieked. 'The Devil is among us!' And with that he jumped over his gate and lit out for his porch. The buckets flew out of his hands. The cold spring water spilled all over the ground.

Next they came to Fiddler John's. The fiddler was sitting in his yard practicing for the square-dance on Saturday. Godsey slowed down again to ask him for a drink.

'It's a horse critter of the Revelation!' John shouted, thinking he'd seen a ghost. And instead of giving them a drink, he fiddled a mad new tune, faster and wilder than anything he'd ever done for a mountain square-dance.

The fast jiggy music from his fiddle got into the mule creature's feet. Godsey pranced off, half galloping, half dancing. He kept on high-stepping it until he reached the door of his own cabin, halfway up the mountain.

When Solomon Shell had caught his breath, they went inside to see Mondie. She, poor woman, was so ashamed to see company coming that she had hidden her head under her apron. There she sat, rocking back and forth in her rocking-chair, sobbing her queer donkey sobs as though her heart would break.

Both Godsey and the wise man had to plead with her before she would take down her apron. When she did at last, Old Sol shook his head. He looked first at the husband and then at the wife, and he shook his head again.

'Tsk! Tsk! Tsk!' he chuckled. 'I'm afraid I can't swap you my shoats after all. There isn't a whole critter between you.'

Sure enough! Godsey had the body and the legs of a mule. Mondie had the head. But there was no neck to connect them!

Now they were in a pickle! The two Scrorses looked at each other hopelessly. They almost cried from disappointment. Were they going to spend the rest of their days as Mule Humans?

'Wait a minute,' said Solomon Shell, stroking his beard and thinking hard. 'There's one last chance. Amber Day poison is devil poison. And there's a cure for almost every devil poison in the Scripture. Let's see what it says about this one.'

So they got the big family Bible down from the mantelpiece. Solomon took it in his lap. He started reading in the first chapter of Genesis. He read through the story of Creation, and the story of Cain and Abel. Then he read through the tales of Joseph in Egypt, and of Moses and the Israelites in the desert. And at last he came to the story of Balaam and the Ass, in the Book of Numbers. Then he stopped.

'Here's your dose of Scripture, all right,' he told them. He read aloud, Numbers XXII, Verse 28: 'And the Lord opened the mouth of the ass, and she said unto Balaam, "What have I done that thou hast smitten me these three times?"'

With that Solomon Shell went out into the woods and cut down a stout oak branch. He stripped it of leaves and twigs. He told the Scrorses to stand quietly. Mondie was frightened and started to blubber again. But he paid no attention.

'It's Scripture, isn't it?' he demanded. 'It's the only cure for Amber Day poison, isn't it?'

Then he took his oaken stick and hit them each three blows. Each time they yelled from the pain. But the third time their mule parts left them.

Yes, Mondie's head and Godsey's legs flew off at the third blow of Solomon's stick. They flew out the door. Somehow or other they melted together as they flew and with one big leap they jumped over the moon. Anyone standing near by

90

could see that that strange mule had cloven hoofs, just like Old Horny's.

When the mule parts had left them, Godsey and Mondie were once again their normal selves. He had his own two legs back in the trousers of his overalls. She had her own head, with her hair pulled tight into a knot.

'Well,' said Solomon Shell, 'I guess that's that. You're all whole again. Now be careful.'

The Scrorses couldn't thank him enough. They begged him to stay for dinner.

'Please stay,' pleaded Mondie. 'You've been to so much trouble on our account. It wouldn't have happened if Godsey hadn't been such an old ——'

But before she could get out the word 'mule' to finish her sentence, both Godsey and Solomon clapped their hands over her mouth. The clock had still another hour to run before the end of Amber Day. They weren't taking any more chances.

Since that time, Godsey and Mondie and all the good folk of the Kentucky mountains have been especially careful of their speech on Amber Day.

Blackbeard

11

UNLIKE most men, who make themselves as handsome as they can, Captain Edward Teach made himself frightful. For Captain Teach was a pirate, and he wanted to look the part. His long, silky dark beard, braided into pigtails and tied with little bows, was looped around his ears. Because of it he was known on the high seas as Blackbeard.

His clothes were brightly colored. At his waist he wore a gay sash, stuck through with three pairs of old pistols. Under the broad brim of his pirate hat he wore a row of matches. Whenever he met an enemy, he lit them. In their dancing light, his black eyes snapped horribly and his ugly grin made fearful patterns of shadow. He looked like something out of a nightmare.

Blackbeard liked to play jokes and then to sit back and laugh until he cried. In his own eyes he was very funny. No one else thought so, however, not even his own wild crew. Although they laughed when he did, they didn't care much for his sense of humor. They recalled too well the time he shot his bos'n, Israel Hands, in the knee. The poor bos'n, who had to spend the rest of his life hobbling around on a wooden leg, didn't see the joke. Teach, however, considered it extremely funny. 'I'm not a bad fellow, after all, boys. What's a little prank between friends?' he roared, holding his sides as Israel stumbled away.

The people of the Southern colonies didn't care for his sense of humor, either. When he swooped down on a seaside farm, stole the cattle, and burned the barn, it was hard for the farmer to see the joke. When his crew roared into a village, shooting their pistols into the air and frightening the villagers out of their wits, the villagers didn't think they were funny at all. From Georgia to Virginia Blackbeard's 'little jokes' were feared and hated.

At last the people of the colonies had enough. They wrote a long letter to the King, telling him of their troubles with the pirates. The King promised to do what he could. Unfortunately, the Royal Navy was weak. England and France had just finished fighting a war, and the King had few ships left with which to punish the sea-robbers. They were almost as strong as the Navy.

Instead of sending out a fleet of ships to wipe the pirates off the seas, the King sent out a warning. He said he would forgive the sea-robbers, if each and every one of them would promise to be good. They could not all, of course, come to London to take the oath to the King in person. They could make their promises to the royal governors of the royal colonies.

Blackbeard saw the notice and sailed up the coast to North Carolina. Here he got down on his knees before his old friend, Governor Eden. He placed his hand over his heart and swore that he would become an honest man. Governor

Yankee Doodle's Cousins

Eden gave him a big sheet of paper with the royal seal on it. It told the world that Blackbeard had been pardoned for his crimes. Then the two men shook hands. History doesn't say so, but they must have winked at each other as they did it.

All the people of the colonies cheered when they heard that Teach would stop playing his jokes on them. But they cheered too soon. As he left the governor, Blackbeard met a merchantman, the *Great Allen*. She was bringing supplies badly needed in the colonies. 'Ah-ha!' roared Teach, lighting the matches under his hat. 'Let's have some fun, boys! Here we go!' With that his ship, *Queen Anne's Revenge*, opened fire. The next thing anyone heard of the *Great Allen* was the story of its wretched crew. Teach had marooned them on a rocky island and burned their ship. He was up to his old tricks again.

Before long Blackbeard had gathered a regular fleet of ships. Beside the *Queen Anne's Revenge*, he had the *Adventure*. This was a smaller ship he captured from an English captain. It was a fast, sturdy little boat. He took its captain prisoner and put Israel Hands in charge of it. Perhaps he felt sorry for his joke on the bos'n.

In the Bahamas he met another pirate, Major Bonnet. Bonnet was a weak man, as pirates go. He was no match for the mighty Captain Teach. When Teach offered to make him his partner, he was delighted. There was a catch in the offer, however. Poor Major Bonnet spent the rest of his career moping in his cabin and walking the deck unhappily, doing nothing. Blackbeard put another man in charge of his ship and made Bonnet practically a prisoner.

With his three ships, Blackbeard felt perfectly safe to play jokes whenever he pleased. The Royal Navy could do no-

thing about it. Once a man-o'-war was sent after him. The pirate only laughed, lit the matches under his hat, drew up his ships for battle, and scared the man-o'-war back into harbor.

His pranks became worse and worse. There was nothing he didn't dare to do. Once, after a battle with other pirates, he needed medicine to heal his men's wounds. His ships were full of gold and booty with which he might have bought what he wanted. But that wouldn't have been much fun for him.

He sailed up the coast until he reached the harbor of Charleston in South Carolina, the richest city in the Southern colonies. Governor Johnson was the bitterest of Teach's enemies. Even so, the pirate sent him a message demanding supplies.

Governor Johnson sputtered. Send supplies to Blackbeard? Certainly not! Right now in the harbor, a ship was making ready to sail for England. On board was a member of the City Council. He carried the governor's message, asking for more help from the King to wipe the pirates off the face of the earth. Send supplies to Blackbeard? Indeed not! Arrest him instead!

When Captain Teach learned that the governor wouldn't give him what he wanted, he only laughed. He thought of a good prank he could play this time.

The Charleston harbor was big and broad, but it had only one narrow opening into the sea. Through this had to pass all the ships coming from and going into the city. Blackbeard drew up his little fleet outside this gateway. One by one the English ships sailed out of the harbor. One by one Blackbeard captured them all. He made prisoners of the passengers and the crews and placed his own men in charge of the ships.

Blackbeard

Among the prisoners was the member of the Council with his message to the King. When Teach saw the message he was tickled even more. He threw back his head and roared. He clapped the poor councilor on the back with a clap that sent him sprawling.

As soon as the Charleston harbor was empty and all the ships were tied up outside, Teach sent his men into the town. They shot their pistols into the air and kicked the people on the shins. They swaggered through the streets up to the governor's palace, where once again they gave the governor Blackbeard's message. 'Medicine and supplies, and be quick about it.'

Governor Johnson did more than sputter this time. He called a meeting of the Council. They sent messengers into the countryside to beg for help against the pirates. But they got little help. Most of the colony's soldiers were off fighting Indians. They sent to North Carolina for help. Here they got none at all. Governor Eden was Teach's old friend. He alone thought his friend's joke was funny.

At last Governor Johnson and the Council had to admit that they were licked. They had no ships nor men with which to fight. Furthermore, they knew that they were in danger. If they didn't give up the supplies, the pirates would turn their guns on the city and send their prisoners to Davy Jones's locker. With heavy hearts the councilors handed over their chests of medicine.

Blackbeard's eyes sparkled with joy when he saw his men returning with the chests. He didn't care much about the medicine, but he thought this the best joke he had ever played.

As soon as the supplies had been put aboard, Teach set his prisoners free. First he kissed all the ladies, and robbed all the men of their money. He nearly split with laughter when he took the governor's letter to the King from the angry councilor. Then he sent the captured ships and their passengers back into Charleston Harbor and sailed away.

All the years that Blackbeard had been sailing the seas he had had no home. Now that he was a very rich man, he began to think that it would be fun to have a fine house and to go about in society. He knew that Governor Eden was his friend, so he went to North Carolina to settle down.

His men weren't very pleased at the idea. When they complained that they had no wish to settle down with him, he played another of his tricks. He landed them on an island in Topsail Inlet. Then with a few of his favorites he slipped back aboard the *Queen Anne's Revenge*. 'Boom!' roared his cannon as it fired into one of the empty ships. 'Boom! Boom!' Again and again it roared until all his fleet, except the *Revenge*, had sunk to the bottom of the inlet. The men rushed to the shore to see what was going on. They could hardly believe their eyes when they saw their captain sailing out into the ocean, leaving them behind. They were marooned with no food; Teach was gone with all their riches.

With his favorites he found a hiding place in another inlet, Ocacroke by name. Here he built himself a fine estate. He bought himself fashionable clothes and a handsome carriage. He trimmed his beard and learned to dance. From the looks of him, as smooth as any dandy, no one would have known that he was the same wild sea-robber who lit matches under his hat to frighten his enemies.

The governor's plantation was not far away. Before long the pirate was an important man in the colony. The other colonists hated him, but the governor was his friend. The two men gave each other rich presents. Soon Blackbeard was

Blackbeard

invited to the governor's balls. All the pretty ladies had to dance with him. If they refused the governor became angry.

You might think that he would have been satisfied with his fine new life. But not Teach! He still liked to play jokes. Now and then he put on his old pirate's dress, gathered his crew, and slipped out to sea. He was still the robber, looking for treasure and sending ships to the bottom. But now he shared his sense of humor with the governor. Whenever an angry shipowner complained and tried to have Teach brought to the law, Governor Eden pardoned the pirate. Blackbeard was grateful and made Governor Eden still more presents.

At last the colonists could stand it no longer. They knew that their own governor would never help them. He was almost as bad as Blackbeard. So they wrote a letter to Governor Spotswood of Virginia, who agreed to help them.

First Governor Spotswood offered a big reward. To anyone who could capture Blackbeard himself, he promised five hundred pounds of gold. For each of the pirate's officers, he promised fifteen pounds, and for each of the men, ten pounds.

This was not all he did, however. Secretly he fitted up two men-o'-war, the *Lyne* and the *Pearl*. He called together his bravest officers and from them picked two, Captain Brand and Lieutenant Maynard, to take charge of the ships. They picked their crews from the best men in the colony.

Silently the two Virginia ships slipped into Ocacroke Inlet. The officers hoped to take Blackbeard by surprise. When they reached the pirate's fine plantation, however, he was waiting for them. His friend, Governor Eden, had sent him warning. From the walls of the little fortress Blackbeard's cannon looked them in the face. Blackbeard himself was standing on the dock, his hands on his hips, enjoying his new joke. To show the Virginians that he had no hard feelings, he invited them to dinner. He had a grand feast prepared for them. When the meal was over he held up his wineglass and offered a toast to their health and good luck.

No sooner had the Virginia officers returned to their ship than Teach's cannon roared and the fight was on. But this time the joke was on Blackbeard. He had not counted on their courage. The battle raged for hours. The pirates on the shore and the Virginians on their ships gave each other shot for shot.

When at last the smoke was cleared away, Blackbeard was dead. All his pirates had been killed except poor old Israel Hands. The Virginians gathered up the treasure which the robbers had hidden away. They loaded it into the holds of the *Pearl* and the *Lyne*, to take it back to their governor, who had promised to return it to the real owners. They took with them Blackbeard's body, to prove that he was really dead. Poor old Bos'n Hands was allowed to go free. He had had enough punishment from the pirate himself.

When Governor Spotswood announced Blackbeard's capture, all the colonists except Governor Eden rejoiced. This time they knew that they were rid of Captain Edward Teach and his sense of humor for good and all.

John Henry

12

OL' JOHN HENRY, the steel-drivin' man, was as big as an oak, as strong as a bull, and as black as a skillet. Some people say that he was a roustabout on the Mississippi, others that he was a fireman on a Mississippi steamboat. But the real John Henry was a railroad man. His story has been told over and over in ballads sung by negroes and railroad men from Roanoke to Altoona.

As a pickaninny, he sat on his old pappy's knee in East Virginny. And his old pappy said to him, 'John Henry, son, yo're gonna be a steel-drivin' man.'

The little black boy smiled up into his pappy's eyes and nodded. Then he looked ahead into the Years to Come and said, 'The Big Ben' Tunnel on the C. & O. Road gonna be the end o' me.'

The Civil War was fought. The slaves were set free. The United States began to grow, spreading from the Atlantic to the Pacific. Everywhere men were chopping down trees, clearing farms, digging ditches, blasting tunnels, and building — houses, farms, factories, bridges, railroads — trying to make room for themselves.

In spite of the prophecy, John Henry went to work for the railroads when he grew up. On one of his early jobs he belonged to a crew which laid the track. They had still a hundred yards to finish when the foreman looked into the valley and saw the 5.15 express heading for them sixty miles an hour. The sun was shining in the engineer's eyes. He failed to see the flags signaling him to stop. In another ten minutes that express train would hit the unfinished track. There was going to be an awful wreck. The foreman waved his arms and yelled. But the 5.15 kept on coming lickety-split.

Then John Henry came to the rescue. He told the other workmen to stand back out of his way. He wrapped the hundred yards of steel track into a coil. Once, twice, he swung it around his head. On the third swing he let go. As straight as an arrow the track shot out into the air and fell to earth right in its proper place.

There was still no time to lose. John Henry grabbed a mouthful of spikes and picked up a heavy hammer in each hand. He ran down the ties as fast as he could go, spitting out the spikes through his teeth and smashing them into place. As he drove in the last spike and jumped aside, the 5.15 rushed past without so much as a jolt. Until he got back to the roundhouse and heard the story, the engineer didn't even know what danger his train had escaped.

As a reward for John Henry's heroism the railroad made him a steel-drivin' man on the Big Ben' Tunnel. The steel-drivin' men were the brave fellows who blasted the tunnels through the mountains. They drove long rods of steel into the heart of the rock to make holes for the dynamite. The holes had to be deep. It took a strong man to hammer a

steel bar into a granite boulder. These tunnelmen were the biggest, toughest, strongest workmen in the world.

Of them all, John Henry proved to be the biggest, toughest, and strongest. With each hammer stroke he could drive the steel twice as far into the rock as the next man. He could strike twice as fast, too. He worked so fast that his helper, Li'l Bill, had to have a bucket of ice water on hand to keep the handles of his sledges from catching fire. Even so, the big steel-driver burned up two hammers a day. Cap'n Tommy, his boss, said proudly that John Henry did the work of four men. He loved him as he loved his own son.

One day a stranger came to the tunnel selling a new-fangled gadget. It was a steam drill. He said it could drill holes faster than three men working together.

'That's nothing,' said Cap'n Tommy. 'You can take your engine and get out. I've a steel-drivin' man, name of John Henry, who can drill holes faster than four men working together.'

The salesman, who didn't know any better, laughed politely.

'Don't waste your time and mine, sir,' added Cap'n Tommy. 'My man can beat your drill to the bottom of a spike any day in the week. Good day, sir.'

The salesman didn't leave. He tried a new approach. 'I'll tell you what I'll do, Cap'n,' he said. 'I'll make a little bet with you. If your man can beat my drill, you may have the drill free, absolutely free. If he can't do it, you buy two drills from me. That ought to be fair enough.'

That touched the Cap'n's pride. He went around to see John Henry.

'There's a man in town who says his steam drill can beat you driving steel, son. That isn't so, is it?' he asked.

John Henry

"'Course not,' laughed John Henry. 'You bring that thing around here and I'll show him.'

Polly Ann, John Henry's pretty yaller-girl wife, overheard the conversation. She remembered the prophecy John Henry had spoken when he was a baby on his pappy's knee. 'Big Ben' Tunnel on the C. & O. Road gonna be the end o' me.' She begged him not to try.

John Henry only laughed at her and said that prophecy was just woman's talk. 'Besides,' he added, 'I'm a steel-drivin' man and I'll beat this steam drill if I lay down my hammer and die doin' it.'

Cap'n Tommy slapped John Henry on the back for joy. The bet was made. The tunnel crew prepared for the contest. John Henry bought a fine new hammer with a twelve-pound head and a four-foot handle. He named it Polly Ann for good luck.

At last the great morning arrived. People came from the mountains of Pennsylvania and Virginia and Kentucky to see the negro race the drill. Polly Ann, in her best blue dress, brought her little pickaninny baby and laid him in the grass where he could see his pappy. John Henry took up his position. Li'l Bill brought the bucket of ice water and stood ready to hold the spike in place.

Cap'n Tommy, in his high silk hat, made a speech to the crowd. At its end he turned to John Henry. 'Son,' he said, 'if you beat that contraption, I'll love you as I never loved my own child. I'll give you fifty dollars and a new suit.'

The onlookers shouted, 'John Henry, you can't beat that drill.'

'Who says I can't?' called back the giant, rubbing his hands together. 'Why, I'll drive my steel into the rock before it gets started.'

Then the timekeeper fired his gun and the race began. Slowly at first, then more quickly the heavy sledges fell. *Chug-chug-chug*, the steam drill drove its spike inch by inch into the rock. *Bom-bom-bom*, John Henry drove his. The only sound in all the mountains was the rhythm of the blows.

The water in Li'l Bill's bucket was soon hissing with steam. The steady thunder of the hammers made some of the country people fear that the mountains themselves were falling down. At the end of the first hour the steam drill was forging ahead. For every *bom-bom*, there came a *chug-chug-chug*.

'Pour some water over me,' called John Henry. So Polly Ann poured cold spring water over his back to wash off the dust. All the while she was doing it he kept on driving, faster, faster, faster.

At the end of the second hour the *bom-chug, bom-chug, bom-chug* sounded like a hurricane. John Henry had caught up with the drill. The muscles rippled under his black skin. The sweat ran in rivers off his nose and his back.

'Li'l Bill, sing to me — and sing fast,' said John Henry. So Li'l Bill sang his favorite hammer song. John Henry kept time.

Now, in the third hour, he pulled ahead. For every two *chugs* came three *boms*. His spike was going deeper than the drill's. The veins stood out on his temples. His blue dungarees were drenched black with sweat. Bill kept on singing and John Henry kept swinging.

And then the crowd began to cheer. John Henry had six inches more to go, the steam drill had a foot. *Bom-bom-bom!* Three inches! *Bom-bom-bom!* Two inches, one inch!

Cap'n Tommy clapped his hands. Polly Ann cried. The mountains echoed with the cheering of the onlookers. John

John Henry

Henry had won! The steam drill had still eight inches to go. Like a great shrieking tornado, the crowd rushed forward to clasp the hero's hand. But it stopped suddenly, in silence.

For there beside his spike lay John Henry, gasping for breath. He'd won, all right. He'd beaten the drill. But with his last powerful stroke, his great heart had burst within him. Polly Ann knelt beside him and placed his little pickaninny in the palm of his hand.

John Henry looked down at the baby, just as his own pappy had looked down at him. John Henry said: 'Son, yo're gonna be a steel-drivin' man. But the Big Ben' Tunnel is the end o' me.'

And with that he laid down his hammer and he died.

Tony Beaver

13

TONY BEAVER, the great lumberjack of the South, lived 'up Eel River.' You won't find Eel River on any maps. The geographers haven't decided where to put it. The people of Louisiana and Arkansas are sure that it's in the cypress swamps. Georgians are just as sure that it's in the turpentine hills. North Carolinians insist that it's in the Smoky Mountains. But West Virginians, who know most about Tony, say that Eel River is high up in their own Alleghenies.

It's not hard to visit the camp, however, if you really wish to see it. Just send word to the lumberjack himself by the next jay bird you see, and Tony will send his path after you.

By the way, this path has an interesting story. One autumn day long ago, as Tony Beaver walked through the woods, something tickled his legs. It felt smooth and ribbony, like a snake. He tried to brush it off, but it clung to his boots and licked at his laces. Glancing down, he saw a baby path, dancing, frisking, romping around him. Tony searched the bushes, expecting to find a mother road near-by. But the path was all alone.

From the way the little fellow wagged its tail and jumped up and down, Tony guessed that it must be lonely. From the looks of its stones and weeds, which hadn't been brushed in a long time, he knew it lacked a mother's care. It was obviously an orphan, just a poor little orphan path that led from Somewhere to Nowhere.

Tony took a fancy to it and carried it gently back to Eel River. Here he gave it food and brushed the cockle-burrs out of its grasses. He let it sleep in front of the fire. In time it became the camp pet. The boys were fond of the clever little thing and taught it a number of tricks. When it became old enough and strong enough, Tony made it his special messenger.

The path still has one bad habit which Tony has never been able to cure. It likes speed. It skims over the hills and down the valleys like a runaway roller-coaster. Some timid people who have visited Eel River say they'd rather spend the rest of their lives at camp than ride home on that streak of greased lightning.

If you aren't too shaken up when you get there, you will find Eel River an unusual logging camp. It's very large, in the first place. After all, Tony and his jacks are big men. In the second place, the bunkhouses look like overgrown watermelons. Instead of the square log buildings you find in Minnesota and Maine, these are shaped like footballs. Their outer walls are smooth and green, their inner walls soft and pink. The bunks and chairs are carved from the same hard black stone as the fireplaces. In case you think your eyes are spoofing you, the bunkhouses really are watermelons.

Before Tony became interested in logging, he had a melon

Tony Beaver

farm. He grew fruit so huge that the hands had to use bucksaws to cut them from the vines. The only trouble with them was they were too big to haul to market. Tony had to think about that problem for several days. While he was thinking he sat by his fire and smoked his pipe. The clouds of black smoke rising from his corncob made the people of Arkansas hide in their cellars. They thought a tornado was blowing up.

Finally Tony figured it out. He built a railroad right up to the melon patch. Three flatcars were hitched together. The smallest melon was rolled aboard. The engine chugged off with Tony Beaver sitting on top of his prize, as proud as you please.

Unfortunately, the tracks ran up a steep grade and down again in a hairpin turn. The engineer, who wasn't used to hauling a load of one watermelon, forgot to be careful. The cars lurched against the hillside. The cargo wobbled unsteadily. Then, whang! The melon, Tony and all, rolled off the flatcars, down the hill, and splashed into Eel River with a kerplunk that caused a flood as far away as New Orleans.

The force with which it hit the water broke the melon into a thousand pieces. For hours the river churned red. It looked as though Farmer Beaver had been drowned. But, no! He simply pulled himself up on one of the seeds and paddled ashore.

As the other seeds floated downstream they caught against the dam by the sawmill. The jam there gave Tony an idea. He made a bargain with the miller, who cut them up into planks and sold them for hardwood. Thus Tony Beaver became interested in the logging business.

He didn't want to waste the rest of those melons. He had his boys roll them to the edge of the field. They dug out the red meat, cut doors and windows, and put in chimneys. Then they built fireplaces of some seeds and carved others into furniture. Lo and behold! There stood as fine a set of bunkhouses as ever was!

The most interesting person at the Eel River Camp is, of course, Tony Beaver himself. He's too great a person to describe. You'll have to see him for yourselves. And until you do, you'll have to be satisfied with stories of some of the wonderful things he's done.

Some years after he'd given up farming and gone into the lumber business, Tony was brought again into the public eye. He still kept a small garden of a few thousand acres on which he raised peanuts. His 'goobers,' as he called them, were sold at circuses and baseball games all over the United States. He had also a stand of molasses maple trees, which produced the sweetest, most delicious syrup you ever poured over a flapjack. They say Paul Bunyan used to send for a small ocean of it every year.

Tony Beaver never could learn to do things in a small way. One season he produced so many goobers and so much molasses that even he was swamped. The circus people complained that peanut shells were heaped so high in the tents the audiences couldn't see the rings. Negro mammies from Richmond to New Orleans moaned that they couldn't fry cakes fast enough to sop up the 'lasses. Even so, the Eel River warehouses were bursting with unsold goods.

To add to Tony's troubles it began to rain. It rained for days and nights without stopping, until the hill country above Tony's private town of Eel River Landing was flooded. At first the townsfolk didn't mind. They found it entertaining to be able to sit on their own front porches and watch henhouses and church steeples sweeping past them downstream.

Still it poured. They began to be alarmed. Their own levees were about to break. It looked as though Eel River Landing itself might be washed out into the Gulf of Mexico.

A committee was elected and sent to ask Tony if he could do something to stop the flood. He shook hands with all the members and sat down in front of the bunkhouse fire to smoke his pipe and think. Soon a Big Idea came to him.

The members were sent home to collect all their friends and relations at the peanut warehouses. The loggers were sent to the molasses stores. Big Henry and Sawdust Sam, his foreman, hitched the big oxen to the vinegar cruet and the salt box, and drove them to the riverside. The big logger himself borrowed a wooden spoon from the cookhouse and followed after.

As soon as everyone had met, Tony gave his directions. The townsfolk shelled the peanuts as fast as they could and tossed the nuts into the river. The lumberjacks emptied the molasses barrels into the water from the other side. Sam dumped in the salt. Big Henry poured in the vinegar. Great Tony Beaver straddled the flood, one foot on one side, one on the other, and stirred that river for all he was worth.

The goobers and 'lasses stuck to the reeds. They clogged the river bed. The current began to slacken. Eel River was oozing, not racing, toward the town.

Then the sun came out, the hot noonday sun. A sweet-smelling mist arose as its rays heated the mixture. Still Tony swished his spoon from bank to bank. Bubbles appeared gradually along the shores, little pearl bubbles at first, then big balloon bubbles. Finally the whole river boiled up. The steam rose higher than the mountains. The odor was delicious!

Tony's spoon churned faster and faster. As the river bubbled and hissed and spouted, its brown speckled waters thickened. From time to time the big lumberjack lifted his ladle and let it drip. Each time the drops fell more slowly, until at last one spun out into a fine hard thread.

With that, Tony Beaver tossed the spoon aside and jumped to the bank. With a jerk he yanked a cloud across the sun. Immediately the river cooled. The thick, sticky mass stopped seething and began to harden. The current had stopped completely. There above Eel River Landing stretched a dam and a broad lake, as brown and quiet and hard as a rock. Except for the white pebbly specks made by the goobers, it was as smooth as a skating rink.

The townsfolk cheered. A holiday was declared and the committee gave Tony a vote of thanks for saving the village. The kids ran home for their ice skates. Soon everyone was gliding in and out among the peanut bumps. People for miles around came to help celebrate.

It was the best party West Virginia ever had, except that there were no refreshments. These were easily supplied, however.

'Break yourself off a piece of the dam,' Tony suggested to a hungry-looking youngster. 'It tastes mighty good.'

The boy thought Tony was joking. But when the big logger reached down and broke off a hunk, he agreed to try it. M-m-m-m! It certainly did taste good. One or two other brave fellows tried it. Soon there was a scramble for the sweet nutty stuff.

Tony had not only saved the town. He had invented peanut brittle.

The Mississippi Valley

Johnny Appleseed

14

THIS is the story of Johnny Appleseed, as strange and lovable a man as ever lived in the American wilderness. Some say that his ghost still lingers in the apple orchards of Ohio and Indiana.

Appleseed, of course, wasn't his real name. His parents proudly named him Jonathan — Jonathan Chapman. Young Johnny Chapman spent his boyhood playing in the woods and on the farms near his Boston home.

As he grew sturdy and brown, two things became clear to all who knew him. First, he was a born orchardman. He understood trees, especially fruit trees. Second, he was going West. He had heard tales of the wonderful rich country behind the Pennsylvania mountains, the country of Daniel Boone and the pioneers. He was going to see it. As a young man he went to Pittsburgh, bought himself a little farm, and planted an orchard.

At that time Pittsburgh was West. Nevertheless it wasn't far enough West for Johnny. Day after day, people passed his farm. They came on foot, on horseback, in rickety farm wagons, in handsome coaches — all bound for the wilderness of the Ohio Valley. Some of them stopped at his door to ask for water, or food, or a night's lodging. To all of them Johnny gave what he could.

Johnny felt sorry for these people. He knew how lonely they were going to be without the towns and pleasant farm-lands they had left behind. He wanted to help them. But how could he, a poor nurseryman, do it? Sometimes he had hardly enough to eat himself.

One night his question answered itself. He'd give them all apple orchards. So he did. To every traveler who stopped at his cabin, he gave a bag of apple seeds. The pioneers were nearly always grateful. They wrote home to their friends about the generous man near Pittsburgh. Soon Johnny had given away all the seeds he could spare. He started bothering his neighbors. Most of them were gruff Pennsylvania Dutch-men. They thought their young friend was a little crazy. But they were glad enough to give him the mash that was left in their cider presses, if he could use that.

Patiently he worked all winter, picking out the seeds from the sticky mess. He dried them with care, and sewed them into little deerskin pouches, to be ready for the rush of spring travelers. When spring came, he left his own farm and went to the waterfront with his treasures. Here, where two rivers meet to form the great Ohio, came the travelers from the East. Some came to ferry across to the dark opposite shore, others to pile their belongings on flatboats which would carry them down to the unknown West. And here Johnny stayed, giving away his 'orchards.' People soon forgot that his name was Chapman. Along the levees and highroads they called him Appleseed.

Johnny Appleseed

Soon Johnny began to worry. If these orchards were really going to grow, they needed a trained orchardman to take care of them — someone who knew how to plant and prune. Who could do that? The answer was simple — Johnny himself. He sold his farm and bought a couple of flimsy canoes. He heaped them full with the cider mash, tied them together with a piece of rope, and went West.

For the next forty years until he died, Johnny had no home of his own. He paddled his little canoes up the creeks and backwaters. Wherever he found a likely spot he stopped. He cleared away the underbrush and planted the seeds from small deerskin pouches. Then he built a fence around his plot, to keep the deer from nibbling the first tender shoots — and off he went again. Several times he ran out of seeds. He had to go back to Pennsylvania for more cider mash, to be dried and sorted and packed in pouches for more orchards.

Now and then when new settlers moved into the countryside, Johnny 'sold' them the saplings from his forest plots. If they had money he charged 'a fib-penny bit' for each tree. But more often than not he took old clothes as a swap, or let the pioneers 'buy' the orchards with promises to pay him later.

As you can see, he didn't make much money this way. That didn't worry him. He didn't need much money. He liked sleeping out in the open. He never wore shoes, even in the worst blizzards. At first he wore the cast-off clothes he received for his young trees. After a while, even these became too civilized. So he begged an old coffee sack from a storekeeper, cut a hole for his head and two for his arms, and let it go at that. Hats were a nuisance, too. Since he had to carry a kettle to cook his cornmeal in, he solved the problem by wearing the kettle.

He had no gun and no hunting knife. Not even the Indians, those master woodsmen, could understand this fact. Johnny, however, lived well on berries and apples and roots and the cornmeal mush he stirred up in his hat. As for shelter? Many an old settler will tell you that when Johnny was invited to spend the winter night in front of his cabin fire, he shook his head politely. He said he'd rather sleep out in the open with his friends the animals.

This strange little man with the odd outfit and the scraggly beard was a welcome guest in all the tepees, lean-tos, and cabins in the Ohio Territory. Wherever he went, he managed to carry little presents for the settlers. These were usually trees and 'yarbs' for the grown-ups, bits of calico for the little girls, and odd pebbles and shells for the boys.

But best of all he had a stock of stories. In the wilderness, news was scarce. The pioneers rarely had news of the neighbors who lived five miles away, news from back home, or news of what was happening in the world. Johnny talked and listened to everyone he met. In time he became a sort of living newspaper and postman for the people in the wilderness.

But the news he liked best to tell was his news 'fresh from heaven.' After he had shared a supper with a family in some lonely clearing, he sat before the hearth and read aloud from his Bible. Sometimes, in his own strange Biblical language, he told about his visions. One granny who listened to him when she was a little girl said he used to make the cabin 'blossom with the roses of Galilee.'

The boys, of course, liked most to hear him tell about his life with the Indians. The Shawnees, a fierce tribe, were still the terror of the Ohio country. Not many of the white settlers had much to do with them. But Johnny really lived with them. It is hard to understand how he escaped harm at

their hands, going about unprotected as he did through the forest. But when you understand the Indians, you can readily see why. The Shawnees thought he was a medicine man. Woe to any brave who touched a hair on the head of a holy person! Once, while camping in the forest, Johnny had met an Indian who was suffering from a fever. Johnny knew well what plants could be used to cure illnesses. In a day or so he had cured the brave. From that time on, the Indian was his devoted friend. He even asked the white man to visit him in his camp.

At first the other Indians were suspicious. They made Johnny prove his worthiness. His body had been so toughened by his life in the woods that he was as strong and courageous as a red man. He stuck pins through his flesh without flinching. He walked barefoot through the snow in the bitter cold weather. He could tell direction by instinct, and he knew as much wood-lore as his hosts. In fact, he knew more than they did. He knew ways of planting corn to make it grow better. He knew how to cure sicknesses and wounds. The red men were amazed when they saw him take a red-hot iron and burn the ragged edges of a gash he had received from a sharp stone. Everyone knew that this was a good way to keep out infection. But how many had the courage to do it?

Johnny was as good an Indian as any of them. So he was made a member of the Shawnee tribe. Throughout the whole West he was known as the Indian's friend.

Many of the stories he told the settlers were about his adventures with animals. He dearly loved all living things. He considered it a sin to kill or to harm any of them. The animals seemed to understand this, and some people thought he understood animal-talk.

124

Johnny Appleseed

One chilly night he was walking through the woods when he began to feel sleepy. He picked out a hollow log and started to crawl in. Unfortunately, a honey bear had had the same idea. All at once, Johnny touched something soft and furry. He heard an angry growl only a foot from his head. You and I might have been frightened. But not Mr. Appleseed. He apologized politely to the bear, backed out of the log, and found himself another shelter in the crook of a tree.

Another evening he sat down beside a little stream and built a fire to cook his cornmeal. As the sun sank and darkness fell, he noticed that hordes of tiny gnats were being attracted by the light. Worse than that, they were being burned in the flames. Johnny was hungry, but he couldn't stand the thought that his fire was taking the lives of his insect friends. 'God forbid,' he said, 'that I should build a fire for my comfort that should be the means of destroying any of God's creatures.' So he put it out and hunted for berries to give him strength until morning.

For several years Johnny had a pet wolf who followed him wherever he went. This was a strange pet indeed, especially in the frontier country. Wolves were hated and feared almost as much as were the Indians. But this wolf was different. Johnny had found him caught in a trap. Its heavy iron jaw had cut his leg. There he lay waiting for an angry frontiersman to come with his rifle.

Johnny Appleseed, however, had no rifle. He walked fearlessly up to the snarling beast and soothed him. Unafraid he pried open the jaws of the trap and set the animal free. Carefully he bound up the wounded leg. He brought water from a near-by spring and gave the wolf a drink from his old mushkettle hat. He treated him as though he were a sick baby. As the sore healed, the wolf attached himself to Johnny. He padded behind him in the woods and watched over him at night. He was the orchardman's friend and favorite until an angry farmer, mistaking him for the thief in his chicken yard, shot him.

Perhaps the most dramatic of all Johnny Appleseed's adventures was his saving of the fort at Mansfield. In 1812 the new United States and the British went back to war. It was a foolish war, but the two nations felt bitterly toward one another. To help themselves, the British got the support of the Indians in the Territories. They felt that the white men had treated them unfairly. They were eager for the chance to fight. Johnny did what he could to persuade the Shawnees, his adopted brothers, to be peaceful. But as much as they loved him, they voted for war.

Johnny himself refused to fight the Indians. He thought of them as foolish children. He knew they couldn't understand what they were doing. Even so, he felt it his duty to help the American settlers. When he heard that the Indians were going on the warpath, he got busy. He traveled night and day through the wilderness. At each frontier cabin he paused only long enough to give his warning. 'Rise up,' he called. 'Take your family to the fort at Mansfield.' Then he quoted from the Bible, '"For behold, the tribes of the heathen are round about your doors, and a devouring flame followeth after them." '

One by one the settlers left their cabin clearings. Some of them fled in their nightshirts, leaving behind all their belongings. They could see the red skies in the north, where the Shawnees were burning farms and towns.

How safe the fort at Mansfield, Ohio, looked to them as they ran out of the forest! Its big blockhouses loomed up at the corners. Its cannon threatened from the walls.

Johnny Appleseed

Unfortunately, however, there was little food inside the stockade. Even worse, there was little water. The village spring was outside the fort. People from miles around had come to seek shelter. When at last all the pioneers had gathered, it was clear that the fort could not hold out for very long. Unless word could be sent to the American garrison at Mount Vernon, thirty miles away, Mansfield was lost.

The captain called a meeting of all the men. He explained how much they needed help. He called for a volunteer to run through the woods to Mount Vernon to ask for help. But the pioneers stood there, silently. The trip to Mount Vernon meant almost certain death. The woods were full of enemies. And even without these, it was a dangerous trip.

Then came a clear, calm voice from the back of the crowd. 'I will go,' it called. It was Johnny. He had already done his part. For days and nights without sleep he had been hurrying through the countryside carrying his warning. He must have been very tired. But here he was again, offering to make the long dangerous journey to Mount Vernon.

The men protested. 'I know the trail,' he said, 'and I shall be safe in the forest. My brothers will not harm me.' Without further ado he was off.

All night he sped on his errand. Worn out, he stumbled into Mount Vernon and aroused the captain of the garrison. Then without rest or refreshment he led the soldiers back. Shortly before he reached the fort, he stopped. He had done his duty, but he refused to take part in the fight. He would curl up in a log and sleep, he said. He was tired. And besides, there was an orchard near-by that needed his attention in the morning.

The soldiers reached Mansfield in the nick of time. The Shawnees had already made an attack. But, sandwiched between the fresh army and the fort, they were soon beaten off.

As the years went by, the Ohio Territories were left in peace. Johnny's saplings grew into large trees. New settlers moved in and cleared the land. The wilderness became a rich farming country, crossed with roads and dotted with villages. Things became too civilized for the strange little man. So he moved West with the frontier into Indiana and Michigan and Illinois. In his coffee-sack shirt and his mush-kettle hat, he planted his seeds in the forests and carried his 'news fresh from heaven.'

One day many years later a farmer found his worn-out old body lying beside a little orchard in the woods near Fort Wayne, Indiana. Johnny Appleseed had died looking after his beloved trees.

Mike Fink

15

I'M a Salt River roarer! I'm a ring-tailed squealer! **Whoop!**
I'm half wild horse and half alligator and the rest of me is
crooked snags an' red-hot snappin' turtle... I can out-run,
out-jump, out-shoot, out-brag... ary man on both sides the
river from Pittsburgh to New Orleans and back again to
St. Louee! Cock-a-doodle-doo!'

Mike Fink, the bad man of the Ohio River, was not at all
modest when he made this famous boast. Whether or not he
was as bad as he liked to think remains to be seen.

Mike started out as a keel-boatman. In his day there were
no steamboats to carry people and goods up and down the
rivers. Instead there were long flat boats, like barges, which
drifted downstream with the current and had to be pushed
upstream by poles and oars. The men who worked on these
keel-boats were very strong. In order to get his job, Mike
had to beat up the rest of the crew. When Baptiste, the
French boss, saw him handing out black eyes and broken
noses, he knew that Mike was the man for him.

Yankee Doodle's Cousins

Mike was as clever as he was wild. He could steer a boat in and out of the snags; he could make her dance over a falls like a lady at a ball. Before long, he was his own master and could lick any other captain between Pittsburgh and New Orleans, as he boasted. He became very famous.

One of the things for which he was best known was his skill with a rifle. With his long-barreled gun, Bang-All, he could shoot the wings off a hummingbird. He proved his skill once and for all when he was a young boy.

Farmer Neal, his friend, had a shooting match. As a prize he offered his best steer, a fat animal which would keep a family in food for several weeks. Anyone could come and shoot for twenty-five cents a chance. All the woodsmen from the countryside came to try their luck. Little Mike came, too, in spite of the laughter of the men. 'What? Let a baby shoot with us?' they sneered. 'You go back home to your mother and make mud-pies.'

This made the youngster angry. All the money he had was one dollar and twenty-five cents. 'I'll take five chances,' he roared at the top of his voice. 'I can shoot better than any of you. You'll see!'

The others laughed all the harder. He seemed to be a brave lad, however, so they agreed to let him take his turn at the end of the contest. One after another the grown men aimed their rifles at the target. By the time they had finished, it was chewed to pieces by bullet holes. Only a diamond-shaped hole showed where the bull's-eye had been.

Then up stepped young Fink. Slowly he raised Bang-All to his shoulder for the first of his five shots. He looked down the barrel at the target, taking his time. After what seemed to be an hour he pulled the trigger. Zing! Right through the center of the diamond flew his bullet.

Mike Fink

The crowd roared. 'That was only luck! You can't do that again! Move the target!'

'All right!' yelled back Mike. 'Move the target. You haven't seen anything yet.'

The target was nailed to another tree farther away. Again Mike took up Bang-All, looked down the barrel, and pulled the trigger. Once more the bullet cut clean through the center of the diamond. The crowd said that the target should be moved even farther away.

After the fourth shot Farmer Neal himself bet that Mike couldn't do it again. 'Leave the target where it is, this time, and let us see if you can hit it,' he shouted. The boy grinned and lifted his gun. He didn't bother to take a careful aim. He banged away.

'Hooray!' yelled the judges as they looked over the target. 'You missed it, sonny. You didn't even touch the paper. Who says you can shoot?'

'Missed it, indeed!' sneered Mike. 'I'll show you if I missed it.' With that he took his knife and dug into the bark of the tree. Out came two flat bits of lead, one on top of the other. The fifth bullet had hit the fourth and driven it into the wood. The young marksman turned around to glare at the crowd. 'Cock-a-doodle-doo!' he roared, beating his chest and flapping his arms. And before the astonished crowd he walked off with the prize steer.

From that day on Mike and Bang-All were the champions. Not many rivermen tried to beat him. Once Davy Crockett challenged Fink to a contest. Davy and Mike had long been friendly enemies; neither would admit that the other was better than *he* was! First Mike aimed Bang-All at a family of little pigs in a near-by pen. One after the other he shot off their tails. 'Pooh!' sneered Davy, 'you left them each a half-inch of tail. I'll finish the job.' So he shot off the stubs as clean as a whistle.

Mike began to worry a little. He couldn't let the hunter from the Shakes of Tennessee win at his own game. Then the boatman saw his chance. Mrs. Fink, a patient woman, walked to the well. As she stood quietly drawing a pail of water, her husband raised his rifle. Bang! The pretty shell comb she wore in her hair broke into two perfect halves. One of them fell to the ground. Mrs. Fink didn't feel a thing.

'Let's see you knock the other half out!' Mike cried.

This was too much for Davy Crockett. No gentleman would shoot at a lady, no matter how well he handled a gun. 'Consider it a draw, Mike,' he said politely. 'I won't try to beat that shot.'

Not only was Mike famous for his shooting; he was famous for his mischief as well. When he saw something he wanted, he didn't bother to buy it properly. Neither would he stoop to stealing like a common thief. He usually got his way through trickery.

The keel-boat was drifting down the Ohio River when Mike saw a flock of fat sheep grazing on the bank. He and his crew hadn't tasted fresh meat for a long time. The sight made him hungry. 'Well, boys,' he roared, 'it looks as though we'll be having a leg of lamb for dinner tonight. Tie the boat in to the shore.'

It so happened that the keel-boat was loaded with barrels of snuff bound for Natchez. Mike filled a bucket with the horrid brown stuff and carried it ashore. He picked out six of the best-looking animals and rubbed their faces in the bucket. Of course, the snuff made the sheep sneeze. Their eyes watered and grew red, and the unhappy beasts ran bleat-

ing around the pasture frightening the others. Then Mike called the farmer.

'Look here, friend,' he said sadly, 'your sheep are sick. They have the Black Murrain. It's a terrible disease. If you don't shoot them right away the whole flock will catch it and die. Why! I've seen thousands of sheep die of this very thing! I do feel sorry for you. To think of losing such fine fat animals!' With that he shed a crocodile tear, and the poor farmer looked worried. He had heard about the dreadful disease that killed whole flocks overnight.

'You'd better shoot them now,' went on the boatman, 'before they give it to the others. And be sure to throw their bodies into the river.'

'Alas! Alas!' cried the farmer. 'What shall I do? I could never shoot the sick ones without hitting the healthy ones. I'm not smart enough with a gun. Won't you shoot them for me?'

Mike pretended to feel badly about the whole thing. He shook his head until the farmer got down on his knees and begged. 'If you'll do this for me,' he sobbed, 'I'll give you two jugs of my best peach brandy.'

At last Mike Fink agreed. He shot the unfortunate sheep and dumped them into the river. The grateful farmer brought the jugs of brandy and said good night. As soon as it was dark, the boatmen fished up the bodies of the sheep, had themselves a fine dinner, and went on their way.

They thought they were safe. A little farther down the river they tried the trick over again. It worked, too. But before long the news got back to the first farmer. He saw that he had been robbed, and he went to the judge at Louisville.

When Mike and his gang returned from their trip downriver, they found that they were under arrest for stealing sheep. Every officer in the country was looking for them. For a long time they were able to hide in a cave beside the river. At last the governor offered a big reward for their capture. The poor sheriff, who needed the money, was a friend of Mike's. He knew where the boatmen were hiding, too, and he went to call on them in a friendly way.

After a long conversation he got Mike to give himself up and to come into court. 'On one condition,' said the boatman. 'I'm not at home on dry land. I have to have my boat under me to feel right. If I can come to court in my keel-boat I'll be very glad to come. And you can have the reward money.'

The sheriff, of course, thought that this was another of Mike's strange jokes. 'Don't look so worried,' snapped the boatman. 'I'll fix it.'

On the day of the trial, the judge and the townsfolk met in the courthouse on the top of the hill. Everyone wondered how Mike would come 'in his boat.' And then they all saw! The big flat-bottomed keel-boat was mounted on wheels and hitched to a team of oxen. All the boatmen stood in their places on the deck with their big poles in their hands. As the oxen puffed up the hill, Mike called out to the sheriff, 'Is everything ready? I can't stay long.'

The sheriff knew that the judge was angry. He tried to tell his friend about the judge's anger. But for all the faces he made Mike and his boys rode merrily on into the courthouse square. What a sight they made as they jumped down from the boat and marched into the room in their red shirts, all shouting 'Cock-a-doodle-doo!'

The boatmen sat down in the front row. The judge scowled at them over his glasses and began to read. 'I charge you, Michael Fink, keel-boatman, with stealing sheep,' he read. All the people in the room scowled at the thieves. It was perfectly clear that Mike and his boys were going to be put into jail for their tricks.

All of a sudden, before the judge could catch his breath to say anything else, Mike jumped up from his chair. He blew a terrible blast on his horn. 'To your places, boys,' he yelled. 'We're leaving.' And with that the boatmen jumped out the window, took their oars in their hands, and pushed the boat, wheels and oxen and all, down into the water of the Ohio River. 'We had a pleasant time,' Mike called up to the judge and the worried sheriff. 'We'll call on you again some day!'

That was the last time that anyone tried to arrest Mike Fink.

Once, it's true, Mike Fink bit off more than he could chew. He was so pleased with himself after his escape from the law that he thought he could do anything. At a river inn he met his old friend and enemy, Davy Crockett. Davy had been boasting about his wife, who wasn't afraid of anything under the sun.

'I'll scare her!' roared Fink. 'I'll bet my Bang-All against your Betsey that I can scare the daylights out of Mrs. Crockett.' The bet was made, and Mike crowed his old crow, 'Cock-a-doodle-doo!' to settle the matter.

He searched through the swamps until he found an old alligator with a horrible face. He dressed himself up in the 'gator's skin and lay beside the road until Mrs. Crockett set out for her evening walk.

As she walked up to him, Mike opened the huge jaws of the 'gator right in her path. She stepped quietly aside as though he were nothing but an old stump. He swished his tail back and forth and crawled up beside her. She paid no attention at all. She certainly didn't look frightened.

This made Mike angry. He rose up on the 'gator's back legs and tried to give Mrs. Crockett an alligator hug. It didn't frighten her at all. Instead it made her angry. She turned around and looked at him with her worst look. Lightning flashed from her eyes. She was awfully mad!

Mike tried once more. He moved closer and tried to hug her again. 'That's enough, you lowly worm!' she screamed. 'Take that!' And with her toothpick she cut off the 'gator's head. Then, of course, she saw Mike inside the beast's skin.

'So that's your trick, is it?' cried Mrs. Davy Crockett, rolling up her sleeves. 'I'll teach you to bother respectable women on their evening walks. Come out and fight like a man!'

Without another word she lit into the bad man. She swung her handbag and kicked and bit and pulled and punched. When the battle was over, she rolled down her sleeves again and went on her way. Poor Mike Fink! He lay there in the swamp, bleeding and sore. 'I'm a Salt River roarer,' he whispered to himself as he counted stars. 'I'm half wild horse and half cock-eyed alligator ...' But the word 'alligator' in his boast sounded feeble. The great Mike Fink, who could crow like a rooster and fight like a wildcat, had been licked. Worse than that, he had been licked by a woman!

Dan'l Boone

16

DURING the French and Indian Wars, General Braddock and his red-coated soldiers marched into the wilderness of western Pennsylvania. General Braddock knew very little about Indians and about the wilderness. As a result his trip was a failure. In his train were two men, however, who could have helped him had he asked their advice. These were two young men, hardly more than boys, who well knew the ways of the wild frontier.

The first of these was a young surveyor; his name was George Washington. The second was a lad from North Carolina who drove a supply wagon; his name was Daniel Boone.

At night around the campfire young Dan'l listened to the stories told by an old scout. John Finley, the scout, had wonderful tales to tell. He had hunted bear and buffalo beyond the Appalachian Mountains. He had dodged Indians on their forest trail, the 'Eskippakithiki,' the 'Warrior's Path.' He had seen the 'dark and bloody ground,' Kaintuck.

Yankee Doodle's Cousins

Although Kaintuck was a wonderful country with rich plains and tall woods, no Indians lived there. It was their battle-ground. There the tribes from the North met the tribes from the South. Neither would allow the other to settle in the lovely country. From their struggles the land took its name.

As young Dan'l listened to John Finley's tales he wanted more than anything in the world to see Kaintuck for himself. Day after day he teased the old scout until the latter gave his promise that some day he would take the boy across the mountains into the 'dark and bloody ground.' Twelve years later the promise was kept.

The rest of the story is well known. Young Dan'l saw Kaintuck and loved it. He led his family and his friends into its great forests. They cleared the woods and planted farms; they built little towns and forts and called the country Kentucky.

Boone did more than explore Kentucky. When people from the Eastern States moved in to share his new land, he felt crowded. His nearest neighbors lived within ten miles of his farm! A man didn't have room to breathe! So Dan'l moved his family again, farther west this time, into the wilderness west of the Mississippi. Here he had all the room he liked. He explored the great plains and the Missouri River Valley. As a very old man he went hunting all alone as far as the Rocky Mountains.

There are many stories, however, that the history books don't tell about Dan'l. There is, for instance, the story of his meeting with his wife.

Dan'l was a great hand with a rifle. Had he lived some years later, he could have taught Mike Fink and Davy Crockett a few tricks. While they were babies in their cradles, he was shooting the pin feathers off the eagles who soared above the Smoky Mountains. Once, so they say, he saw a wildcat leap upon a frontier baby. The wildcat thought he was going to have a tender bit of meat for his dinner. But Dan'l drew his gun to his shoulder, pulled the trigger, and Mr. Wildcat fell dead. The baby wasn't even scratched.

This adventure made Dan'l dislike wildcats intensely. Whenever he had the chance, he did his best to rid the woods of the mean beasts. One winter evening, as he returned to his father's home from a hunting trip, he saw two bright green eyes shining at him from the forest. They were wildcat eyes, he was sure, so he dropped to his knee, drew his gun to his shoulder, and sighted down the barrel. The green eyes shone brighter than ever. But something made Dan'l hold his fire. Those bright green eyes were different from the others that had stared at him. Instead of shooting, he walked bravely up to the beast to have a closer look.

Imagine his surprise! The eyes weren't wildcat eyes after all. They belonged to the most beautiful girl Dan'l had ever seen. There she sat crouching in the bushes. She was perfectly calm and not at all afraid, even though Dan'l had started to shoot her. By the time he had taken a second look at his 'wildcat,' Boone was head over heels in love. He took the girl back to the settlement, and soon they were married.

Dan'l wasn't very good at book learning. His spelling was hardly of the best. For many years a sample of it could be seen in the bark of a tree. Here he had carved this message, 'D. Boon cilled a bar,' as a record of his bear-hunting. He could read his own messages, however. Most of them were notches carved into trees.

As a young hunter he made three notches in the bark of an ash sapling to show where he had spent the night on a hunting trip. Then he went his way and forgot all about them. Twenty years later, after he had explored the whole state of Kentucky, a group of men came to him. They were having a great deal of trouble over a piece of land. The deed to the land said that its boundary began 'at an ash marked by three distinct notches of the tomahawk of a white man.' But no one could find the ash tree.

The men knew that Dan'l had been hunting in the country and thought he might have put the marks on the tree. They asked him to help them find it. Dan'l, of course, had marked hundreds of trees in the twenty years that had gone by. He scratched his head and tried to recall which tree this could be. At last he remembered.

The country had changed greatly since Boone's hunt. Where once had been wild forest, now were farms and fields. Nevertheless, Dan'l took the men to the spot at which he had started his trip. Through woods and over streams he led them until they reached a large ash tree. Not a sign of a notch could be seen on its bark. The men shook their heads; they thought that Boone had made a mistake. But Dan'l knew better. He walked around the tree until he found the right spot, took his hunting knife and cut away the bark. There, right under his cut, were the three notches that had been made when the tree was a slender young sapling.

The most exciting stories about Dan'l Boone have to do with his escapes from the Indians. Although the latter were his enemies, they admired him and thought that he had magic powers. On his first trip into Kaintuck he was surrounded by a party of braves on the Warrior's Path. They were out to kill anyone who dared get in their way. Boone had nothing but a knife with which to defend himself; the braves had guns. He started to run away from them through the forest, dodging this way and that, trying to cover his tracks. They followed him. Suddenly he disappeared. His tracks disappeared, too. Not a sign of the hunter could they find. They decided that it must be one of the spirits who had led them on this merry chase. As they turned back to their war party, Dan'l laughed to himself in the top of a tree. He hadn't vanished at all; he had saved himself by swinging up into the air on a wild grapevine.

Another time he was crossing a grassy meadow when a shot rang out above his head. An Indian had fired at him from the woods. Dan'l had no way of hiding himself. It was too far to run to the cover of the forest. 'Bang!' spoke the Indian's gun, again and again. Dan'l could hear the bullets zing past his ear, but none of them touched him. How did he save himself? As he told the story, he waited for the brave to fire. When he saw the flash from the gun, he knew just where the bullet would go; he was able to duck out of its way.

His luck was not always good, however. Once in a while he was caught by his enemies. Even then he managed to get away from them. At times he talked the Indians into letting him go. Once he pretended to swallow his hunting knife and made the braves believe that he had magic powers. That time they set him free as fast as they could. No Indian wanted to make a magician angry!

Before many years were over, Dan'l had met and escaped from so many Indians that he knew most of them by name. He enjoyed matching his wits with theirs. He liked to tease them about his escapes. A group of Shawnees made up their minds to capture him once and for all. They crept up to the edge of his farm clearing and waited for a chance to catch him. Soon they had their chance.

On his farm Dan'l grew tobacco. When the leaves had

reached the right size, they had to be hung in a shed to dry. Farmer Boone chose this very day to untie the bunches of dry, brown tobacco leaves that hung from the rafters of his barn. The braves saw him leave his house, and knew that their time had come. He had no gun with which to defend himself.

As he worked high up in the rafters, the Indians entered the barn and demanded that he give himself up. Dan'l saw that they had him where they wanted him, but he refused to surrender. He pretended to be very humble. He greeted the braves in a friendly way and asked them for one last favor. Before they took him away, he wanted to finish untying the tobacco. When this was done, his family could sell the leaves and have a little money with which to live when he was gone. The braves, who admired his coolness, agreed to this. They settled themselves on the floor of the barn and Dan'l went on working above their heads. From time to time he asked about their wives and families, told them bits of gossip about other Indians he had seen, and soon had them chatting pleasantly.

All at once, before they could see what had happened, Dan'l dropped an armful of the brown tobacco into their up-turned faces. The leaves broke into bits as they fell; the dust filled the whole barn. The Indians coughed and spluttered, their eyes watered, and they gagged on the stinging brown dust. Quickly Dan'l jumped down from his perch and ran to his house. Here he could defend himself. Once again he had tricked his friendly enemies; the poor braves had nothing for their trouble but red eyes and raw throats.

These Shawnees were the very ones who had captured him years before during the Revolutionary War. At that time, the settlements in Kentucky were no more than little forts.

Dan'l Boone

Dan'l's own village of Boonesborough had only a handful of men with which to defend itself. Its few log cabins were built inside a stockade. The settlers depended on the hunters to supply their food.

Boone knew that the woods were full of Shawnees who were working for the British. Even so, the fort needed food and he agreed to get it. As luck would have it, he ran into a party of braves who took him captive and marched him through miles and miles of wilderness along the Warrior's Path to their home in northern Ohio. Dan'l knew that he was in great danger. The British had set a price on his head because of his help to the American colonists. He had little chance of escaping from the war party, which guarded him carefully day and night. His only chance was to make friends with his captors.

Dan'l behaved like a perfect prisoner. He showed the Shawnees as many tricks as he knew. He gave them his word that he would not try to escape. Soon they trusted him so much that they allowed him to walk freely without thongs to bind his hands. By the time they reached their village, they wanted to make him a member of their tribe.

First Dan'l had to undergo many tortures. He had to run through a line of braves, each of whom slashed at him with a whip. His bravery and his strength were enough for them. He was as good an Indian as any of them. So he was taken into the tribe and the Shawnees called him their brother.

Before they had captured him, however, the Shawnees had promised to turn him over to the British commander in Detroit. Whatever else might be said against them, the Indians kept their promises. Therefore Dan'l's new brothers took him to the British headquarters. The commander was well pleased, for he knew that Boone was his most dangerous enemy in the West. He put him in irons as a prisoner of war.

The Indians had come to be so fond of their new tribesman that they hated to see him taken prisoner by the British. With their reward money they paid his ransom, and once again he was free.

He was not really free, however. During his stay in Detroit he had heard plans for an attack on the settlements of Kentucky and Western Virginia. All the tribes from Ohio and Indiana were to gather together to make one huge war party. The British were to give them guns and bullets. Then they would attack the little frontier forts and give the settlers no mercy. The Shawnees knew that Boone had heard of these plans and that he would try to warn his friends.

Therefore they kept a sharp lookout whenever Dan'l went hunting. They still treated him as a brother, but they made him stay within their sight. Whenever he was given powder and shot for the hunt, he had to return what was left to the tribe. They took no chances on his having powder with which to shoot his way out of camp.

Nevertheless Dan'l was too smart for them. He managed to steal powder for himself. Instead of using a full portion of it for each shot on the hunt, he used a half portion and hid the rest. Soon he had enough for his purpose. On a dark night he sneaked away from the camp, ran silently through the forest, and headed for Kentucky.

The journey was long and hard. He had to cut through bramble patches and swamps to avoid Indian trails and the braves who were looking for him. He did not dare to shoot game for food. The sound of his gun would tell the Indians where he was.

After days of hardship he reached Boonesborough. How he longed to see his wife and children! Poor Dan'l! When he reached the settlement, they were not there. Thinking he was dead, they had returned to their old home in North Carolina!

He had little time to think about this misfortune, however. He had work to do. The fort had to be gotten ready for a long battle. Other settlers had to be warned. Food had to be collected. Men had to be sent for help.

Almost immediately the Shawnees appeared. The battle was fierce. Weak and weary as he was, Dan'l Boone fought with the others until he was wounded. Then from his bed he directed the battle.

At length the noise of the battle stopped. Boonesborough had been saved, and Dan'l was able to take his well-earned rest. The war party's plans had failed. Kaintuck, the 'dark and bloody ground,' was saved for the United States. Some day it would become Kentucky, the peaceful country of rich towns and grassy meadows.

Davy Crockett

17

WHEN Davy Crockett went to Congress, he didn't waste his time making dull speeches. He told stories. He had a great many stories to tell, too — stories of his life as a hunter, a backwoodsman, and an Indian fighter. Sometimes he was carried away by his stories. People began to expect almost anything from him.

His fame spread far and wide. During his second term in Washington, it was feared that the world was coming to an end. Halley's Comet shone in the sky. This was a particularly bright comet with a long tail. It came fearfully close to the earth. Bits of burning metal flew off and showered fields and forests. The sky was streaked with shooting stars.

This comet had appeared before. Whenever it came close to our planet something dreadful happened. People feared it meant disaster again. But with Davy in Congress they thought they might be safe. They sent a committee to him, just as people send committees to Washington today. They asked him to help them. At last he agreed. If the comet came any closer, said he, he would climb to the top of the Appalachian Mountains. There he would stand until he could catch the old comet and wring off its tail. This made the committee feel better and they went home satisfied.

Davy Crockett was born in the Tennessee hills. As a tiny baby, he was cradled in the shell of a snapping turtle. His crib cover was a panther's skin. A crocodile curled itself up into a ball for his pillow. From the very beginning he was a remarkable person.

As a young man he fought in the Indian Wars. All over the Tennessee and Arkansas country he hunted coon and bear. He even tried his hand at farming. Everything he saw and did gave him a new story to tell.

Throughout the Shakes, as his part of Tennessee was called, Davy was famous for his grin. It spread from ear to ear. No one could look at it without smiling back. People thought that it had strange powers, and told how Davy had once grinned a coon out of a tree.

On the top branch of a pine sat the fat little coon, grinning like a Cheshire cat. Davy needed a new cap. He liked the markings on the little creature's tail. But he had left Betsey, his long rifle, at home. All he could do was to stand there and grin. He stretched his lips as far as they would go and fixed his snapping eyes on the coon. After an hour the animal gave up. The glare from Crockett's smile was too much. Down fell the raccoon. He had been out-grinned by the hunter.

On another occasion in the Shakes, Davy saw another coon. This time he decided to grin him down for the fun of it. Davy grinned and grinned, but nothing happened. He stood there all night long, grinning. Rattler, his hunting dog, who usually went wild with excitement when his master hunted a coon, acted very strangely. He paid no attention, but curled up at the foot of the tree and slept soundly.

In the morning, Hunter Crockett saw his mistake. What he thought was a coon was only a big knot on the branch. What a fool he had been, grinning at a tree all night long! His grin had not been wasted, however. It had burned all the bark off the tree.

Beside Rattler and Betsey, Crockett had two unusual hunting companions. His favorite was his old bear, Death Hug. Davy had brought him up from a tiny cub. He had a saddle and bridle made for the old creature and often rode him around the wilderness. Death Hug saved his life on one occasion. Davy was surrounded by angry Indians, who were out for his scalp. As soon as the bear saw the danger he leapt into a tree with his master on his back. From branch to branch he swung, faster than the Indians could follow. He crossed the whole forest this way and came down in friendly country.

The second was an alligator whom he called Mississippi. Davy and Death Hug were skating on the frozen Niagara River, above the falls. It was getting on toward spring. Without any warning, their piece of ice broke off from the rest and headed for the falls. They were indeed in a pickle! But Death Hug saved the day. Davy locked his arms around Death Hug's waist. He guided the chunk of ice over the great waterfall and they landed safely at the bottom, without even a ducking. The trip had been such great fun, Davy wanted to do it again. So he called Mississippi and jumped on the alligator's back. The powerful 'gator took a long running start and hopped right up over Niagara.

Davy loved animals and the animals all loved him. They even elected him to Congress. His rival was a very rich man who lived on a big plantation. He had been to college and knew how to make long important speeches. He used big words and impressed the voters. He dressed in a long frock coat and a big silk stovepipe hat. Crockett was only a poor hunter from the Shakes. He had nothing but his buckskin hunting dress and his coonskin cap. The voters all flocked around the rich man.

The animals felt sorry for their friend. They went to work for him and told him not to worry. Whenever the rich planter got upon a platform, guinea hens and bullfrogs gathered at the foot of the stand. Wild turtle doves and pigeons collected in the trees overhead.

As soon as he opened his mouth to speak, up went a chorus. 'Cr-ck-tt! Cr-ck-tt! Cr-ck-tt!' croaked the frogs. 'Cr-ck-tt! Cr-ck-tt! Cr-ck-tt!' clucked the hens. 'Cr-ck-tt! Cr-ck-tt! Cr-ck-tt!' cooed the doves and pigeons.

Davy stood on the side-lines and grinned. The voters were charmed. They stopped listening to the speaker on the platform and went off to vote for the backwoodsman.

Davy once gave a party for the birds and animals on a Fourth of July. He gathered them together under the Liberty Tree. In a long, flowery speech he thanked them for their help and told them how much he loved his country. He wound up with twenty-six big cheers for Uncle Sam and the states. There were twenty-five states in those days. Then he added two little cheers for Texas and Oregon, which were almost states, but not quite.

The birds and animals listened quietly. They paid more attention than did the members of Congress in Washington.

After the speech, Davy taught them all to dance. Death Hug and Mississippi moved among the party dancing with all the guests. Ben Hardin, Davy's friend, whistled all the dance tunes he knew.

This Ben Hardin was Davy's best friend in Congress. They had known each other for a long time. They first met on the Mississippi River. Davy was paddling his log canoe when he spotted a strange craft, floating toward him. It was a raft with several kegs nailed together on top. Sitting on the kegs was a little fellow in a sailor's dress, with a sailor's pigtail hanging down his back.

It looked as though the two crafts were going to crash, but neither Davy nor the stranger would give way. Each began to swear at the other and to tell all the awful things he would do to him. They became so mad at one another that there was nothing to do but to fight it out.

They paddled to the shore and went to it. After the battle they shook hands and became friends. The stranger said his name was Ben Hardin. He was so wild that when he wanted a rest, he leaned against a cyclone.

Soon after this a Western cyclone hit the river. It roared along the bank and made straight for the two new friends. Poor old Ben! For all his bragging, he was scared. Davy laughed, however. He grabbed a piece of lightning as it went by, greased it with rattlesnake oil, and jumped on its back with Ben hanging to his coat-tails. Off they flew across the cyclone and landed in the Shakes near Davy's home.

Ben and Davy lived together for a long time. Sally Ann Thunder Ann Whirlwind Crockett, Davy's beautiful young daughter, kept house for them. Then Ben fell in love with an Indian girl. He loved to dance. The Indian was the only girl in the world who danced well enough for him.

Davy didn't like the match. Nevertheless, he made an offer to his friend. If Ben could dance longer than the

Indian, she could be his bride. The old sailor agreed at once.

Davy invited his neighbors to the contest, which was held on Asphaltum Flats. These flats were so hard that lightning split into bits when it hit them. The fiddlers went to work. They played polkas and jigs and hornpipes and reels. They played everything from 'Weevily Wheat' to 'Pop Goes the Weasel.' Ben and the Indian girl whirled around and around so fast they soon became invisible. Even the Flats began to smoke from the beating of their feet. At last Ben had to give up. His pigtail wilted, and he fell in a heap, coiled up like an anchor chain.

Remarkable as all these stories are, they are commonplace compared to Davy's stories about the sun. His best adventure took place during the Winter of the Big Snow, shortly before Davy Crockett was killed fighting the Mexicans at the Alamo. The weather became frightfully cold. Everything in the world was frozen fast. When Davy tried to strike a fire, the sparks froze. Even the daybreak froze solid. Davy tried to keep warm by racing up and down the hills and singing himself a song about 'Fire in the Mountains.'

This is his own story of what happened. 'Well, after I had walked about a hundred miles up Daybreak Hill I reached Peak o' Day, and there I discovered what was the matter. The earth had actually frozen fast on her axis and couldn't turn around, and the sun had got jammed between two cakes of ice under the wheels, and there he had been shining and working to get loose till he was frozen fast in his cold sweat.

'"C–R–E–A–T–I–O–N!" thought I. "This is the toughest sort of suspension, and it mustn't be endured — something must be done or human creation is done for." It was so cold

Davy Crockett

on top of Peak o' Day that my upper and lower teeth were all collapsed together as tight as a frozen oyster. So I took a big bear off my back, that I'd picked up on my road, and threw him down on the ice, and soon there was hot sweet bear oil on all sides. I took and squeezed him over the earth's axis until I'd thawed it loose, and I poured about a ton of sweet bear oil over the sun's face. Then I gave the earth's cogwheel one kick backward till I got the sun free, and whistled, "Push Along, Keep Moving." In about fifteen seconds the earth gave a grunt and began to roll around easy, and the sun walked up most beautiful, saluting me with such a wind of gratitude it made me sneeze.

'I lit my pipe by the blaze of his topknot and walked home, introducing people to the fresh daylight with a piece of sunrise in my pocket.'

The Big Bear of Arkansas

18

THE big steamboat *Invincible* pushed up the Mississippi River from New Orleans. Its back paddle churned around and around, sending out a wake of white bubbles. On deck stood a traveling man and a hunter. The hunter was a famous man along the River. He was called the Big Bear of Arkansas. No one remembered his real name.

The hunter was pointing out a certain spot to the traveling man. He called it the Forks of Cypress. 'Right there,' he said, 'right there I had my best adventure. Right there I shot a creation bear.' Whenever a pioneer tried to describe something that was too big for his imagination, he called it a 'creation' creature.

That evening the Big Bear of Arkansas told his story.

When he first came to 'Arkansaw' he was a green young boy. He knew very little about hunting and tracking. He soon learned a lot, however. He discovered the tracks of deer and panther and bear. In the fall, when the animals are getting their new coats, their hides itch. The bears have the worst time of it. They rub themselves against the wild sassafras trees, trying to ease the awful itch. Bunches of their hair are caught in the bark. A good hunter can tell the size of a bear by the height of these bunches.

One day, the hunter explained, he was walking through the forest, looking for bear, when he came to a sassafras tree. High above his head, at least eight feet above the ground, was a bunch of black hair. 'Creation!' he yelled. 'No bear could have scratched his back up there. It's either a joke or the biggest bear in all the world.'

He thought no more about it until he found another such mark, deep in the forest. This time he could hardly believe his eyes. 'If there is such a bear,' he said to himself, 'I'm going to hunt him. I'd certainly like to have his skin to make myself a blanket.'

He found no other trace of the big beast, however, and after a few days' hunting he returned to his farm. Here he found things in a sad state. Buzzards were circling about the sky over his cornfield. His pigs were squealing their little heads off. His biggest sow was missing.

In the field he saw the remains of his sow. All about the place where she lay were tracks, bear tracks, the biggest bear tracks he had ever seen.

At once he knew who had stolen his sow. It must have been the big bear, the one whose marks he had seen in the forest. No other animal could leave such tracks. He vowed that he would kill that critter. If he didn't do it, he swore by creation itself that he would die in his own tracks or go to Texas. He didn't know which.

The first time he chased the bear, he had no luck. All he found were tracks and bunches of hair high up on the sassa-fras trunks. Not even Bowie Knife, the leader of his hounds,

The Big Bear of Arkansas

was able to follow the big animal to its den. When the hunter returned to his farm, his big hog had been killed. There were the bear's big tracks.

'I'll get you yet,' muttered the hunter. He renewed his vow to catch the 'varmint' or go to Texas or die.

Three times he hunted the big animal without any luck. The bear became so bold that he came to the pigpen and stole his dinner, even when the hunter was at home. He ran away so fast that the hounds couldn't catch him.

This made the hunter furious. He thought so much about the big bear that he couldn't eat. He wasted away to skin and bones. He couldn't sleep. His hair began to turn gray. Still the big bear robbed his pigpen.

At last the hunter could stand it no longer. He picked up his gun. He called his hounds. He started out into the woods and swore he would never come back until he got his bear. His neighbors said 'Good-bye,' all except one. The one was a greenhorn named Bill, who had lately moved to Arkansas. He knew almost nothing about hunting and thought he might help.

The hunting party started out at sunrise. Very soon Bowie Knife was on the scent. He snuffed along the ground with the other hounds after him. Before long they were deep in the forest.

At last they found the bear. There he sat in the crotch of a tree, about six feet above the ground. The dogs raced to the foot and barked up at him. He sat there as quiet as a pond in low water.

The hunter and his friend took aim. The greenhorn shot first. His bullet struck the bear in the forehead. This was a foolish thing to do. It made the animal angry. His skull was so thick it didn't hurt him much. He climbed down

from his crotch, snarling and growling. All but one of the
dogs backed away and waited in a wide circle. That one was
a young pup. The bear lifted his paw and batted him out of
sight.

Then the hunter took perfect aim. He had to do something
quickly to keep the angry beast from charging him and his
hounds. He fired his gun, but nothing happened. Click!
Click! The gun snapped. It had no cap to fire the powder.
The hunter felt through all his pockets, but not a cap did he
find. He was worried for fear the bear would attack his dogs.

Instead of turning on the dogs, however, the bear jumped
over them and ran away. After him went the hunting party.
As they ran the hunter felt something bobbing against him.
It was the box of caps which had slipped into the lining of
his coat through a hole in his pocket.

On and on ran the bear until he reached a little lake.
Splash! In went the dogs after him. They raced to an island
in the center. The two hunters looked about for means of
crossing the water. At last they found a log and paddled
themselves over. This time the greenhorn let his friend fire
first.

Bang! The hunter pulled his trigger. Again the bear was
merely wounded. He rushed out of the thicket with Bowie
Knife hanging on to his fur. He tried to swim back to the
mainland, but the dog held him fast.

At last the hunter shot him through the heart and the
beast sank to the bottom of the lake. The two men rigged
up a grapevine as a rope and hauled the carcass to the shore.
They had killed the wrong bear! This critter was a big she-
bear. It wasn't the 'creation' bear at all!

As usual, when the party reached home, the buzzards were
circling over the cornfield. A pig was missing from the pen.

The Big Bear of Arkansas

Worse still, the neighbors had gathered at the cabin to laugh at the mistake. They made jokes about a hunter who couldn't tell a big bruin from a little she-bear. They offered to buy him glasses. They told the greenhorn to give his friend a couple of lessons.

This made the hunter angrier than ever. In front of all the people from the country he repeated his vow — to kill the creation bear or die or go to Texas.

He spent a long time making ready for his next hunt. He rested his hounds. He cleaned and oiled his rifle and made sure that he had plenty of caps and that the holes in all his pockets were sewed up. On Monday morning he started out. He left a note on his cabin door, telling his neighbors that he had gone. If he hadn't returned by sundown, they could have his farm, he said. He would never come back without the bear.

And then a strange thing happened. The creation bear climbed over the cornfield fence not a hundred yards away. He ambled as slowly and carelessly as though no one were around. Right for the pigpen he headed.

The hunter took aim and fired. His shot struck its mark. The critter wheeled and tore away. He didn't jump over the fence, he ran right through it. Into the woods he crashed with the hounds after him.

By the time the Arkansaw hunter reached him, the big creation bear was dead. It was the right bear this time. He lay there like a mountain. It took five men and a mule to carry him back to the clearing. His skin was so large it covered the bed, with several feet left over on each side to tuck under the mattress.

When he finished his story, the hunter sat quietly for a moment staring at his pipe. 'He was a beautiful critter,' he went on. 'Yes, sir, I reckon he was a real creation b'ar. I never could understand why he gave up so easy at the end. My private opinion is that that b'ar was an unhuntable b'ar, and died when his time come. Or maybe,' he added with a twinkle in his eye, 'he knew when he'd met his match.'

Pirate Jean Laffite

19

BARATARIA sounds like a country in a comic opera. In the early 1800's there was really such a land. At the mouth of the Mississippi in Louisiana, the waters of the river and the Gulf of Mexico form a large swamp. It is full of hidden islands which in those days were full of pirates.

The pirates of Barataria were a gay lot. They captured ships from Spain and South America, made their crews walk the plank, and brought the fine silks and wines and jewels to their kingdom of Barataria. Then they sent notices to the people of New Orleans. 'Come buy our fine wares. Cheap.' The people, who always liked to find a good bargain, flocked out to the market places in the swamp, bought up the stolen goods, and went back home feeling pleased with themselves. They thought the pirates were good fellows.

The boldest of the buccaneers was Jean Laffite. His brother had a blacksmith shop in New Orleans. He became very rich at his evil trade, and rode about the city in a fine coach. He wore beautiful expensive clothes, and danced at all the finest balls. Meeting him, you would never suspect that he was the leader of a rabble gang of cut-throats.

He was a tyrant, in spite of his dainty manners. Two things he insisted upon. The first was perfect obedience. None of his pirates dared to question any order given by the fearful Laffite. Secondly, he could not stand being called a pirate. He preferred the name of privateer. There isn't much difference between the two. A pirate attacks anyone he wants to. A privateer pretends that he is attacking an enemy of his country. Jean Laffite had a letter from the little country of Cartagena. This said that all Spaniards were enemies, and that it was all right for him to attack them. This made him a privateer.

Unfortunately Jean sometimes forgot to stick to Spanish ships. Once in a while he captured a prize that was flying the American flag. He claimed that he loved the United States and that his mistakes made him terribly unhappy. His unhappiness, however, didn't prevent his kidnapping the crew and stealing the cargo.

At last the American Government grew tired of Laffite's antics. The governor of Louisiana offered a big reward for his capture. This didn't bother Jean. He put on his best brocaded vest and his finest lace shirt and swaggered into the city. He even leaned against a wall on the main street, right under a placard that said, 'Five hundred dollars reward! Jean Laffite, dead or alive!'

'Pooh!' he sneered. 'The governor insults me. So I'm worth only five hundred dollars, am I? I'll show him what a real gentleman can do. I hereby offer fifteen thousand dollars for the capture of the governor.' He flashed his white teeth in a disarming smile and bowed politely.

The governor heard about it and choked with rage. He

called in the United States Navy and sent them to blow up the kingdom of Barataria. They had no luck, however. Their boats stuck in the swamp. They lost their way in the bayous. Laffite's men scattered into the wilderness and the Navy had to give up the search.

Then came the War of 1812. The English and the Americans fought up and down the Atlantic coastline, through the Great Lakes, and in the Gulf of Mexico. The English commander heard about Laffite. Because the American Government had put a price on the pirate's head, he supposed that the pirate would be only too glad to help the enemy. With great dignity, as though he were calling on a real king, the English commander put in to Barataria.

Jean received him royally. He gave a great feast for his guest. After dinner the two of them talked over the war. The Englishman told Jean of his plans to capture the city of New Orleans. He offered him thirty thousand dollars and the title of Captain if he and his gang would join the British forces.

Jean listened with attention. When the commander had said his say, his host thanked him for the offer and said that he would have to think it over. The commander went back to his ship sure that he had won a friend.

Meanwhile, Jean, who did love the United States in spite of his pirate's trade, wrote down all that the commander had said. He sent this in a message to General Andrew Jackson, who was defending the city. Furthermore, he offered to bring his cut-throat crew to help fight the British.

At first, Jackson was shocked by the message. Have a gang of pirates fighting for him? Not he! He'd rather go down to defeat than to have anything to do with a blackguard like Jean Laffite!

Pirate Jean Laffite

Later, however, when the British attacked, he felt differently about it. He sent for Laffite. The pirate gang came quickly to the aid of the city. The men fought bravely. No general could have asked for better, more loyal soldiers. In spite of the posters offering a reward for his capture, Jean Laffite was the hero of the day. His loyalty and courage had saved New Orleans from the British!

Jackson apologized to the king of Barataria. He wrote a long letter to President Madison, telling him of the privateer's heroism. The President replied by pardoning Laffite and all his men for all the crimes they had committed.

After this, you might suppose that Laffite would have given up his smuggling and his piracy. With a city at his feet he could have become very rich as an honest man. But not Jean! He soon fell back into his evil ways. Before long the Navy had to send another battleship to Barataria. The captain threatened to shell the pirates' lair, and Laffite was forced to move away.

No one heard of him for a while. But soon ships began again to be captured on the Gulf. Laffite had gathered together an even larger crew of cut-throats. He had built himself a little settlement at Campeachy, where the city of Galveston is today.

Here he was the absolute king. He lived in a large rambling palace called the Red House. This house had been built for Jean by the Devil himself. One dark night the pirate had looked up from his feasting to find the fiend standing beside him. The Devil made an offer. He would build a beautiful mansion for Jean, if Jean would sacrifice the very first living thing he saw in the morning.

Jean was delighted. He agreed to the bargain. The Devil went away to build the palace. Jean meanwhile made his own plans. There was a litter of ugly yellow pups in the yard. He called in his slave and had a pup brought to his bedside. When he awoke in the morning, there lay the puppy, a poor thing, but a living creature.

The Devil was furious when he saw how Jean had cheated him, and vowed that he would have his revenge. Laffite didn't care. He declared a feast in honor of his new home.

After many years of piracy Jean Laffite disappeared. No one knows truly what happened to him. Along the whole coast of the Gulf of Mexico, however, appeared stories of hidden treasure. People had seen mysterious figures walking up the shore carrying chests and spades. Others stubbed their toes against bricks of silver hidden in the beds of streams.

One old couple were having breakfast when three masked figures pushed through their door. The bandits sat down at the table and demanded food. The poor old woman had to serve them her last bit of bread and milk. Without a thank-you the three stalked off into the woods. An hour later as the goodwife and her husband sat shivering with fear, back came the tallest of the three. He drew his pistol and made the couple promise never to speak a word about their unwelcome guests. Then, flinging a dirty package to the floor, he strode away.

When the old people recovered enough to pick up the package, they found inside a thousand dollars in gold.

Even more amazing was the story told by an old soldier. On a grim, stormy night he rode along the gulf shore near the town of Laporte in Texas. It was cold and dark, and as he looked for a place to camp, he heard a thin piping cry. He followed the cry and came upon a deserted farm. In the barn were a herd of goats, huddled together to keep warm. In their misery they were trampling underfoot a tiny kid.

Pirate Jean Laffite

The old soldier picked up the kid and warmed it under his coat. He hitched his horse to a post and looked about for a place to sleep. The little kid bleated as though he were trying to give the old soldier a message. The man let him down and the kid led the way to a broken-down house.

Even in the gloom the soldier could see that this had once been a lovely mansion. He pushed open the door and lit a match. There, under the cobwebs and piles of dust, he could see the outlines of fine pieces of furniture. A fireplace was piled with wood, ready to be lighted. This was indeed good fortune. The soldier made himself a good fire and soon fell asleep in front of it, wrapped in his greatcoat.

How long he slept he did not know. In the middle of the night he awoke to find a tall man standing over him staring into his eyes. He was dressed in a long dark cape which covered a beautiful old-fashioned suit, with brocaded vest and lace cuffs.

He motioned to the soldier to follow him. He led the way through the old mansion, through one room after another, until he came to a small cellar hidden away at the back. Here he stopped and bent over to the floor. He lifted a trap-door by its heavy iron ring.

Suddenly a light shone from the hole. There beneath his feet the old soldier saw an open chest filled with magnificent jewels and old Spanish doubloons. Bolts of silk were piled against its sides. It was a treasure beyond belief.

The eyes of the strange visitor sparkled as he looked into the chest. Suddenly he began to speak.

'I am the spirit of Jean Laffite, the pirate,' he said in a hollow voice. 'This treasure and even more was mine. Now I can find no peace. For fifty years I have been wandering about the world trying to atone for my evil deeds.'

The poor soldier was frightened by the ghostly voice. He looked about for some means of escape, but the ghost barred his way. 'Do not be afraid,' went on the spirit. 'I want your help. I shall not harm a hair of your head. All this treasure is yours.'

'Mine?' cried the startled soldier.

'Yours indeed,' answered the hollow voice. 'But it is yours on one condition. You must take it out to the world and use it for the good of mankind. It must all be spent to help the poor and the sick and the helpless. Only when it has all gone for this purpose shall I find peace.'

Here the ghost's voice became sad. 'But if so much as one penny's worth is spent for selfish pleasure...' He did not finish the sentence. Instead he wept bitterly. The trap-door clanged shut. The poor old soldier had to pick his way back through the darkness to his fireside, wondering what had happened to him.

At first he thought he was dreaming. He lay down again and fell asleep. Once more he awoke to find the ghostly figure looking down upon him. 'Do not forget,' it moaned. 'Until the treasure has been spent for mankind, I can find no peace.' With this he wailed again and disappeared into the gloom.

In the morning the old soldier awoke and looked about the house. True enough! He soon found the cellar and the trap-door with the heavy iron ring. The door was shut tight.

He mounted his horse and galloped into town. There he told his friends about his strange adventure. They were greedy. As soon as they heard the story of the treasure, they hurried out along the road he had taken. They found the house the soldier had described. But nowhere could they find a sign of the treasure. Instead, they were frightened away by the moaning of a ghost.

Over and over again the ghost groaned, 'Not a penny's worth must be spent for selfish pleasure... Not a penny's worth...'

And because he had betrayed the secret of the ghost, the old soldier was never able to find Laffite's treasure.

Febold Feboldson

20

THE state of Nebraska, for all its golden wheat, has had its troubles. When it was first settled, the country around Alkali Lake was upset by a mysterious sea serpent. Giganticus Brutervious, as the monster was called, lived in the bottom of the lake. Every day he rose to the surface and ate twelve yearling calves from near-by farms.

Giganticus was a terrible creature. He had a head like an oil barrel and great green eyes that flashed real fire. His face was so frightful that the sun hid behind a cloud rather than look upon it. Storms and tornadoes raged whenever he flicked his ears. The mere flip of his tail made the farmers for miles around horribly seasick.

A dude Yankee stopping at an Omaha hotel wouldn't believe the story. 'A sea serpent in this desert?' he roared. 'Oh! oh! oh! I can't stand it.'

The Nebraskans, being perfect hosts, decided to show him They set up a fishing camp beside Alkali Lake and invited the Yankee to spend the night there, free. Before morning, however, he staggered back to town, too frightened to speak. His hair had turned pure white. All he could do was to write on a slip of paper, 'It's perfectly true.' Then he fainted.

The Nebraskans stood for the monster as long as they could. He grew bolder and bolder. He swallowed an island from the middle of the lake. That was too much! The farmers elected a Committee to Investigate Giganticus Brutervious. They met and thought about the problem. They went out to the lake in the daytime and walked around stroking their chins. At night they raced back to Omaha to a safe spot in the courthouse.

It was decided that the lake should be drained. When the water was gone the monster had to go, too. The Committee offered one thousand dollars to anyone who would drain the lake. The Drainage Company asked four thousand dollars for the job. The Committee thought about it and said, 'Fifteen hundred dollars.' 'Not a penny less than thirty-five hundred,' said the Company.

While they were dickering, the monster disappeared. Giganticus Brutervious has never been seen since. The following winter the icehouse keeper found a mermaid frozen in a cake of ice. Perhaps she was the monster. Who knows?

Once rid of its sea serpent, Nebraska had other troubles ahead. For a while a bully named Antoine Barada ruled the Missouri River Valley. He was as kind-hearted as a baby, but as restless as a tiger. The worst thing about him was his temper. He lost it twenty times a day. For instance, he watched a pile-driver driving a forty-foot pile into the bed of the river to build a wharf. It was very slow work, of course. Suddenly Barada lost his temper. He picked up the big machine and threw it into the state of Iowa. With his fist he slammed down on the great pile. He slapped it down so far it hit an underground stream and made a well. The water spurted fifty feet into the air.

Barada's pranks, however, were nothing compared to the damage caused by Febold Feboldson. Poor old Febold! He was a kind-hearted, gentle fellow who meant well. But nothing ever turned out right for him. Every time he tried to do the right thing, he caused more trouble.

Originally Febold Feboldson had been a lumberjack for Paul Bunyan. He worked for Paul at the time the great lumber boss filled his camp with Swedes. Hels Helson, Anders Anderson, Lars Larsen — anyone with a name that ended in 'son' or 'sen' could get a job at his camp.

Soon Febold branched out for himself. He moved to Nebraska and started to work on his own. He did very well for a time, too, until his bad luck got the upper hand. The unfortunate fellow had a marvelous collection of animals. He would have been a great success in the circus business. The first of these strange beasts was the hide-behind. No one has ever seen one, not even Febold. It made a practice of hiding behind the loggers when they worked in the woods. No matter how quickly they turned around, the hide-behind turned just as quickly. There it was, hiding behind them and looking over their shoulders. This was annoying, to say the least. The only way that a logger could rid himself of the troublesome creature was to find a filla-ma-loo bird. This bird flew backwards over the logger's head. No hide-behind could stand to be seen by the filla-ma-loo bird, and so the logger could work in peace.

Then there was the hodag, sometimes called the huggag. Paul Bunyan had sent the first of these to Febold in the hope that it might help him get rid of the coyotes. This beast had been bred on Pinnacle Mountain, before Paul sold the mountain to Pecos Bill for the Perpetual Motion Ranch. In order to live on the mountain, the hodag had two short legs and two long ones. Out on the flat plains of Nebraska, the poor things were unable to stand up. There were no trees for them to lean against, so they proved to be entirely useless.

The coyotes finally met their match in the whimpering whingdings. The coyote, as you may know, is a sad creature. He sits on his haunches and bays at the moon as though his heart will break. Febold thought that the best way to get rid of them was to finish the job and break their hearts. The whingdings did it. Their whimper was heart-breaking, all right! It was a cross between the bellow of a spanked baby and the yip of a hurt puppy. The whingdings gathered beside the Dismal River and whimpered until the coyotes felt so bad they sneaked off into the Colorado Mountains and haven't been heard from since.

After the whimpering whingdings came the happy auger. A gay, light-hearted creature he was. He looked something like a kangaroo with a corkscrew for a tail. His job was to bore post holes. As you know, the ground in Nebraska is terribly hard. It's almost impossible to bore a hole for a fencepost. Febold bought some of the ready-made holes Kemp Morgan made out of his duster, but these didn't go very far. Then he tried the auger. The poor animal was gun-shy. Febold crept up behind him and fired his six-shooter into the air. The auger was so frightened he jumped up six feet and landed on his tail. The corkscrew bored into the earth and made a perfect post hole.

Alas! One of Feboldson's neighbors bought a machine gun in Kansas City. He fired it at the auger to see him jump. The *ra-ta-tat-tat* of the gun scared the wits out of the animal. He leapt into the air twenty feet at a leap until he disappeared

Febold Feboldson

over the Rockies. That was the last anyone ever saw of him.

The most useful animal Febold ever developed was the bee-line ox. He had been given the job of straightening the line between Kansas and Nebraska. At first he was stumped. He plowed a furrow with his oxen, but the furrow was crooked. Then he crossed the oxen with a bee. A bee always flies in a straight line. When he had produced a perfect bee-ox he hitched it to the plow and tried again. This time the furrow was straight, a real bee-line, as you can see on the map.

In spite of his success with birds and animals, poor Febold Feboldson was pretty much of a failure in other ways. After leaving Paul's camp, he bought a prairie wagon and a team of oxen and spent several years carrying pioneers across the Western wilderness to the gold rush of California. He did well at this until the year of the Petrified Snow.

The snow swept down and covered the whole state of Nebraska. Then it turned to stone. Traveling was impossible, and Febold, who made his living traveling, was having a very hard time of it. None of the pioneers would budge from the tavern stoves in Kansas City. Febold put his wagon on a sled, but still no one would hire him to make the trip West.

At last he thought of something. He drove out to the Arizona Desert and filled his wagon with its burning hot sand. This he carted back and poured on top of the stony snow. The heat from the sand melted the hard stuff and warmed the air. Soon Febold's customers got up from their firesides and agreed to hire him again. A great success, he thought.

He was wrong. When he returned from California he found that the sand had burned right through the snow to the ground. It had burned away all the trees and shrubs and plants in the whole state. Nothing would grow at all, and the heat was terrible.

When the kind-hearted soul saw what he had done to his dear Nebraska he was wretched. Instead of a rolling prairie, here was a barren desert where nothing bloomed. He swore that he would spend the rest of his life trying to right the wrong he had done.

He built himself a little sod shanty on the banks of the Dismal River. He tried to persuade the pioneers to stop and make their homes in Nebraska. If a few people would live in the state it might not be so bad. But the people wouldn't stop. They had their hearts set on the gold to be found in California.

Then Febold sent to Peru for a cargo of goldfish. He dumped these into the Dismal River one dark night. The next day he ran out to the rolling wagon trains. 'Stop! Stop!' he cried. 'I have found gold in the rushing streams of this beautiful state of Nebraska!'

The word 'Gold!' caught the pioneers' attention. They stopped their wagons and rushed to the riverbank. Eagerly they dipped their pans into the stream. The flashing of the fish looked like the gleam of a thousand gold flakes. But when the pans were lifted out of the water, there was no metal in them. Nothing but fish scales! The gold-crazy pioneers were furious and kicked Febold for all his pains. He couldn't understand why.

After his goldfish plan had failed, Febold tried to do something about the grasshoppers. Along with the burning sand from the Arizona Desert had come thousands of the insects. What the sands didn't burn, the grasshoppers ate. Perhaps people would stay if he could rid the state of these pests.

He heard that flying fish liked to eat them, so he brought

in a school of the lovely silvery things. The fish ate the grasshoppers, but the fish were worse than the insects. The skies were full of them.

Now Febold had to do something about the fish. Every time he tried to make things better, he made them worse instead. He brought in timber wolves to eat the fish. The wolves did what they were meant to do. But without any timber around they became homesick. They spent their time howling. The noise drove people away. Then Febold planted cottonwood trees to make the wolves happy. The cottonwood trees bloomed cotton all over the state. Soon planters from the South heard about the crop and sent their negroes out to pick it.

At last it looked as though Nebraska was going to have some settlers. The negroes loved the easy pickings. The cotton grew so thick they didn't have to bend over to pluck it. When the lower branches had been stripped bare, Febold tried to please the pickers by bending down the top branches.

Unfortunately, those bent-over branches kept growing down into the ground. Only the trunks remained on the surface. The cotton pickers gave up and went back home to the South. The timber wolves hated to lose their trees and began to dig down into the earth to find them. Poor old Febold! He was right back where he started. The wolves dug holes all over the state and when they came up they had changed into prairie dogs. Grasshoppers or prairie dogs — what difference did it make?

At last he stopped trying to mend his mistakes. He went back to his shack on the Dismal River and sat down to think. If only he could find something, anything at all, that would bring back the green grass and waving grain to his dear Nebraska!

The next moment he had the right answer. Rain! Yes, that was it! If he could make it rain, the grass would grow green again, and people would come to live on the prairie. But how could he make it rain?

The Indians made a great noise, shaking rattles and beating drums, whenever they wanted to attract the rain. It nearly always worked. Febold had no rattle and no drum. He'd have to think of something else. Frogs, of course, made a big racket with their croaking.

The problem was solved. Febold Feboldson gathered together all the frogs from the dried-up Dismal River. They refused to croak at first. He had forgotten that they croak only when it is raining. But this didn't stop him. He put the frogs under a spell. Gently he stroked their heads and murmured into their ears, 'It's raining. It's raining. It's raining.' He said it slowly at first, then faster.

Before long the frogs believed him. They had fallen under his spell so completely that they thought it really was raining. One at a time they croaked, softly and timidly, then loudly and boldly. The noise grew and grew. And then came the miracle. The sky became gray with clouds. A low roll of thunder sounded and a wind blew up from nowhere. Splash! A few drops at a time, then a light shower, and finally in a cloudburst came the rain. Nebraska was saved!

Poor old Febold Feboldson stood out in the storm and clapped his hands for joy. At last his, and Nebraska's, luck had turned!

The West

Kemp Morgan

21

BULL COOK MORRISON kept a food stand in Snackover, Oklahoma. It was an ordinary little shack beside the highway. Most of his customers were 'boomers,' the tough fellows who worked in the oil-fields.

One afternoon his door opened with a bang. In came two boomers quarreling with one another. Each claimed that he was tougher than the other.

'You're not so bad,' sneered the first. 'Just watch me. I'll show you what it is to be tough... Oh, Bull,' he called, 'bring me a four-pound roast of beef, done rare.'

A four-pound roast is enough for any middle-sized family, with hash left over. But the second boomer wasn't impressed. 'That's nothing,' he snorted. 'Hey! Bull! Bring me that side of cow you've got hanging in the icebox. And don't bother cooking it. Just scorch the outside... Humph! I'm no sissy.'

Poor Bull hesitated to waste his good meat on these boasters. He was sure they couldn't eat all they'd ordered. But the boomers threatened to roast him instead of the meat if he didn't hurry.

Then the door opened again. In strode a giant as big as the Statue of Liberty. He was dressed in greasy overalls and his face and hands were smeared with oil.

'So you think you're tough, do you?' he roared at the two quarrelers. 'Say, Bull, bring me a live steer and a carving knife, will you? If there's one thing I can't stand it's cooked meat.'

He turned around and frowned at the boomers. 'Want to fight, either of you?' he asked politely. With that he rolled up his sleeves and showed a muscle as thick as a tree trunk.

'N-n-n-no, sir,' mumbled the frightened boomers. Their faces had turned whiter than Bull's tablecloths. In perfect step they climbed down off their stools and backed to the door. Once outside, they took to their heels and vanished in a cloud of dust.

As soon as they were gone, the giant called Bull aside. 'That about the live steer was just a joke,' he laughed. What I really want is a pair of T-bone steaks, well done.'

Poor Bull, who had been shaking in his boots ever since the giant entered, breathed a sigh of relief. He cooked the steaks perfectly, with exactly the proper amount of onion and gravy. The giant licked his lips when he finished his meal. 'Ah-h-h!' he sighed, wiping his mustache. 'That was really delicious. Permit me to introduce myself. My name is Morgan, Kemp Morgan. Could I interest you in taking a job as my personal cook?'

Kemp Morgan! Bull flushed at the very mention of the name. Why! Kemp Morgan was the most famous man in all Oklahoma. He was the man who had discovered oil. So many stories had been told about him that no one believed in

Kemp Morgan

him any more. He was like Santa Claus. And here he was in the flesh!

Poor Bull stuttered and stammered with pleasure. If the King of England had asked him to come to Buckingham Palace to cook the Royal Breakfast, he couldn't have been more flattered.

After a long conversation, Bull agreed to become Kemp's cook. First he protested that he wasn't good enough to cook for so great a man. Then he said he didn't know how to cook for a whole crew. All he knew was how to cook short-orders and sandwiches. When Kemp explained that there wasn't any crew, Bull felt better. Kemp himself did all the work. He was the only one to be pleased.

Kemp was as good as his word. He was the only member of his crew. Rather, he was a whole crew rolled into one person. As Bull got to know him better, he realized that the stories told about the giant were not half wonderful enough. He was a regular miracle of a man.

In those days, before better means were invented, men located oil by 'divining rods.' The oil, of course, was hidden in pools deep under the ground. People who thought they had special powers used to go about the oil-fields with forked sticks. When the stick turned in a certain direction, they marked the spot. Then they told the owners to drill their wells in these places. More often than not, these 'divining rods' were wrong. But it was the only way anyone knew to discover the oil.

Kemp Morgan had his own method. He walked across the fields with his nose bent down to the ground. Now and then he stopped in his tracks. He snuffed and snuffed like a hound on the scent of a rabbit. If the proper smell came to him, he knew that he had found an oil pool. He was always right.

Sometimes he bought up the land on which he had smelled oil. Sometimes he gave it away to other persons. He was a very generous man. Besides, he liked to go about smelling oil, for the very fun of it.

When he spotted a well for himself, however, he went to work. An oil well is not an easy thing to bring in. It takes a whole crew of trained men working together to drill the rock and manage the engine and build the derrick and the tanks. But Kemp needed no help. First of all he dug into the ground with a long-handled spade. When he had dug a narrow hole as far as the spade would reach, he took his sharpshooter and shot a further hole. This saved him a great deal of extra labor.

Into the bullet hole he placed his drill. Down, down, down through the rock he hammered the drill until he struck the pocket of oil. Then quickly he mounted his engine and built his derrick. An ordinary derrick was like a toy compared to his. These were as tall as the observation towers from which forest rangers watch for fires. One of them reached the sky. Like the mast of Stormalong's ship, it had to be hinged to let the sun and moon go by.

As soon as Kemp had finished his derrick he built tanks to hold the precious oil. Then, when a column of black liquid squirted up through the well, single-handed he put on the heavy metal cap and let the oil drain off into his tanks.

Bull Morrison used to stand on the side-lines and watch. His mouth hung open in admiration. Never had he seen anything like this. He almost always missed the capping of the gusher, however. As soon as Kemp was through with his morning's work, he wanted his dinner. Bull had to have it ready the minute the boss had washed the oil from his hands.

Some of the wells Bull watched Kemp bring in were indeed

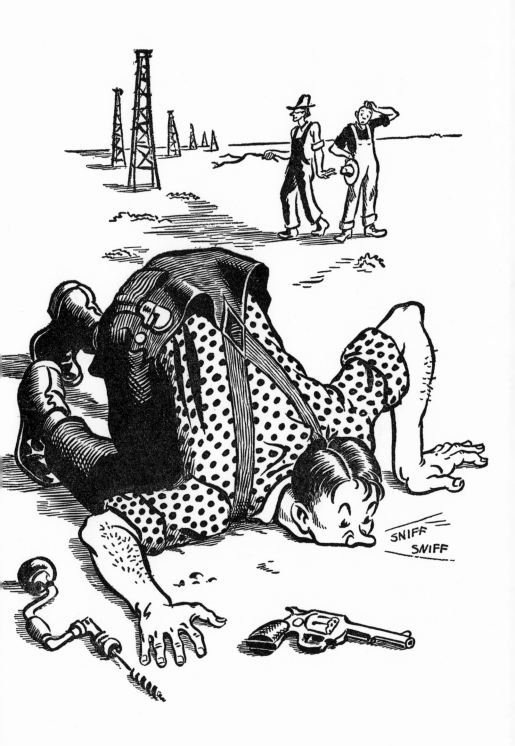

SNIFF
SNIFF

wonderful. Some of them were strange. Only once did he bring in a 'duster.' A duster is a well that spouts gas instead of oil. It blows dry, hot fumes off into the sky, and then nothing happens. No oil follows the gas. The poor oil man has nothing to show for all his pains except a deep, empty hole in the ground.

Once Kemp brought in a duster. At first he was terribly disappointed. Kemp was never one to mope about his misfortune. He scratched his head and tried to think what he could do with the dry well. At last he had an idea. The farmers of Kansas were always complaining about their ground. It was so hard they couldn't dig holes in it for their fence posts. Without good, deep post-holes, of course, their fences were always blowing over in the wind.

The very thing! Kemp sawed up his well into lengths. He loaded these onto a train and sold them to the Kansas farmers as ready-made post-holes. They were delighted to have them and paid Kemp a very good price.

The following winter, Kemp brought in a gusher on the day of a big freeze. The air was so cold the oil froze as it spouted. There it was — a big, shiny black pillar rising out of Morgan's newest derrick. It was easy to handle. Kemp broke off a piece and smelled it. It was perfectly good oil.

Then he had an idea. Usually he sent his oil East in big tank cars. The freight charges for these were very high. Flatcars were much cheaper. But you certainly can't ship oil on a flatcar.

This was Kemp's chance. He sawed the pillar into lengths, just as he had sawed up his 'duster.' He loaded the cold, black bars onto flatcars and shipped them to the distillery. With that money he saved, he bought a whole packing-house full of T-bone steaks.

Kemp Morgan

The queerest well of all was an accident. The giant had to be careful not to hit his hammer too hard. Once in a while he forgot, and his drill went deep into the center of the earth. On one occasion he was swinging at his drill. He was daydreaming at the same time. Harder, harder, harder he swung. At last one powerful stroke slammed the drill right through the center of the earth, like a needle through an apple-core. The other end came out in Brazil in the middle of a rubber plantation.

For days the new well gushed pure rubber. Men came from all over the United States to see the white milky stuff pouring into Morgan's tanks. At last a rubber man from Akron, Ohio, heard about it and made Kemp a handsome offer. Kemp, who liked a chance to turn loss into profit, was only too glad to sell.

Like many of his friends in Oklahoma, Kemp Morgan had several adventures that had nothing to do with his business. Often he had reason to make trips across the sandy plains and deserts. On one of these trips he made camp on the open prairie as the sun was setting. He hitched his mules to a sapling. He dug a little hollow in the sand near-by for himself. Soon he was fast asleep.

During the night a sandstorm blew out of the west. The wind howled about him. He had to cover his head with his saddle blanket to keep his face from being scratched by the flying sand. Throughout the storm he lay curled up as best he could. Finally he fell asleep.

In the morning the ground on which he was lying was full of holes. The sand dunes about him were gone. Furthermore, his mules were gone. He thought he'd been carried off to a strange place. What on earth should he do next? He had no idea where he was.

Yankee Doodle's Cousins

Then, from above his head, he heard a familiar braying sound. Hanging from the top of the sapling by their halters, at least forty feet above him, were his mules. The storm had blown away forty feet of the topsoil. Kemp, resting on the ground, had sunk with the sand without knowing it.

He reached up with his powerful arms and bent the young tree over to the ground. The mules were a little weak in the knees at first, after their night of hanging in space. But soon they were able to walk and Kemp went on his way.

The tale which most Oklahomans enjoy telling about their hero is about the time he brought in the biggest gusher in the world. For years he had gone about the countryside smelling oil. Only once had he missed a gusher. Everyone in the state had faith in him. When he stopped and snuffed the ground, people rushed to the land offices to buy up the land. Or, if they owned it already, they rushed to the banks to borrow money for equipment.

In a little-known part of the state lay a wide prairie. Here Kemp stopped one night to make camp. As he bedded himself down, his nose began to twitch. There was the old smell of oil. Millions and millions of barrels of oil, right under him.

He had already as many wells as he wished. Instead of buying up the land he told his friends about it. Out they raced to the prairies. Each of them bought a section of ground and drilled in his well. They drilled down one hundred feet. No oil! They drilled down two hundred feet. No oil! They drilled down three, four, five hundred feet. Still no oil!

Some of them became cross with Kemp. They thought he had been joking. But when they complained to him, he shook his head. 'That's the biggest oil field in the whole world,' he insisted.

Kemp Morgan

Nevertheless, no matter where they drilled nor how far they drilled, they found no oil. Some of them had sold their homes to buy drills. They were hungry. Their children were going ragged. Kemp felt sorry for them, but still he insisted that this was the biggest oil field in the world.

At last the men became really angry. They marched to Kemp's house and threatened to have the law on him. They showed him their worn-out clothes and their hungry children. There was nothing for Kemp to do but to buy in their land. He paid each man enough money to pay for his equipment and to start life over again.

Then Kemp went to work. He had to prove to himself that he was right. He dug down with his long-handled spade. He shot his sharpshooter into the hole. He put in the drill and hammered as hard as he could. Bull Morrison kept count as he drilled deeper and deeper. He went down one mile. The smell grew stronger and stronger. He went down two miles. Three miles. Bull became discouraged. He begged Kemp to stop drilling. 'You'll wear yourself out,' he kept saying.

But Kemp paid no attention. He drilled down four miles, four and a quarter, four and a half, four and three quarters. Still no oil, but the smell grew strong and clear. 'It's coming! It's coming!' he yelled back at Bull. 'Get out of the way!'

Just as Kemp's drill marked the fifth mile, the rock broke under it. From the center of the earth came a loud rumbling and whishing! A cloud of gas and steam roared up through the narrow well. And then came the oil.

It spouted up to heaven. It drenched the whole state of Oklahoma. And all the men who had sold their land back to Kemp Morgan gazed in sorrow at the gusher that might have been theirs.

Kemp was so pleased he made no effort to cap the gusher. He just let it gush. He stood off to one side admiring it, and saying, 'I told you so . . . I told you so.'

At last something had to be done about it, however. The angels complained that the floor of heaven was flooded with oil. The clouds were greased so that they slid and slipped around in the sky. There were thunderstorms and cloud-bursts all over the country.

Slowly and sadly, Kemp went to work again and fastened on the cap. He hated to do it. His gusher had been such a lovely gusher.

Then he felt more cheerful. He had made up his mind what to do with his oil. He loaded it into tank cars and sent it off to the East. He bought himself a new store suit and went to New York. When he received his money, he bought all the chewing tobacco he could find. He was going to give it as presents to his friends, the oil men of Oklahoma.

But on the train back Kemp Morgan fell to day-dreaming. By the time he reached Oklahoma he had chewed up all the tobacco himself.

The White Mustang

22

FOR over a hundred years, a wild white horse has roamed
the Western plains. The Indians saw him before the
White Men came. The Wild West cowboys and their brothers
the Mexican *vaqueros* have been trying to catch him ever
since. Some people think the Lone Ranger has tamed him
and called him 'Silver.' But for all their 'Hi-yos!' I don't
believe it.

Only one person has ever touched the white mustang. She
was an old, old lady when she told the story to her grand-
children.

Her family came to Texas in a covered wagon when
Gretchen was a very little girl. With other pioneers they
moved westward over the dusty plains, day after day. The
oxen that pulled the wagons moved very slowly. There
were no roads; the crude wooden wheels bumped over the
hillocks and sank into the sand. The sun was hot. The dust
and the sand covered everything in sight.

It was hardly a comfortable trip. For a tiny child of four

it was very tiresome indeed. No one could blame little Gretchen for whimpering and fretting. By the time the wagon train reached the *Llana Estacada*, which is the Spanish name for the Great Staked Plains, she had grown so restless that her mother lost patience.

The family had an old blind pack mare named Nelly. Nelly plodded along after the wagons, carrying sacks of cornmeal. She was a gentle animal with a slow gait.

One morning they let Gretchen ride on the meal bags on Nelly's back. To keep her from wiggling and falling off, they tied her securely to the pack. She thought it much more fun than riding in the wagon.

During the day one of the carts broke a wheel. While the men were repairing it, they turned the horses out to graze beside the river. Gretchen, tired out from her ride, soon fell asleep. She didn't awaken when Nelly wandered off from the others.

The hungry old mare followed a strip of green grass to the riverbank. The cool sandy riverbed soothed her tired feet. On up the stream she moved, munching the fresh grass.

Then Gretchen awoke with a start. From across the stream came a loud, proud whinny. Nelly lifted her head. Her ears pricked up. She sniffed the air and whinnied back.

Across the water stood a beautiful white stallion. His body was the color of fresh cream. His long white mane and tail shone like silver thread. He whinnied again and stamped his hoof, as much as to say, 'Come! Follow me! I am your king!'

Old Nelly pranced and capered like a baby colt. She plunged into the river and swam through the rushing current. Up she bounded onto the bank and galloped after the lovely horse. He paced across the prairie as though he were

196

on wings. After him flew the blind mare, with Gretchen tied to her back.

The stallion led them on and on into a deep canyon. Gretchen cried, but the wagon train had been left far behind and there was no one to hear her. The two horses paid no attention.

Finally they stopped in a grassy glen where hundreds of mustangs were feeding. The wild horses caught sight of the strange old mare and sniffed the cornmeal in the bags on her back. Soon they were clustered around her, nipping the sacks and trying to get at the grain. Poor little Gretchen's legs were scratched and bitten by the hungry broncos.

The white stallion came to her rescue. He fought off the others. With a couple of quick bites, he loosened the ropes that tied Gretchen to the mare's back. He picked her up in his strong teeth by the back of her dress and set her on the ground beside a little spring. There the tired little girl fell asleep.

In the morning, she was alone in the glen. Strangely enough, she wasn't frightened. Everything seemed to be quite all right. She heard a familiar whinny, and there stood Nelly, but without the grain sacks. Gretchen clapped her hands with joy. The mare rubbed her nose against the little girl's neck.

Unfortunately the child was too small to climb up on the mare's back. She tried once, twice, and three times. Her arms weren't long enough to reach.

Without a warning hoof-beat, the white stallion appeared. Again he picked her up by the back of her dress and set her gently, oh, so gently, on Nelly's back. Before Gretchen could reach out to pat him in thanks, he was gone.

That was the last she saw of him. The blind mare wan-

The White Mustang

dered safely back to the worried parents. Gretchen was very, very hungry, but otherwise none the worse for wear.

No one else was ever so lucky as to touch the white mustang. But everyone in the West, from the Rio Grande to Saskatchewan, knew about him and had a story to tell. A few, a very few, had seen him.

The Indians thought he was a spirit. Perhaps the Manitou, the greatest spirit of all, rode unseen on his back. Their arrows passed through him as easily as through air. He raced across the grass-fires in valley after valley. Always he came through without so much as a scorch. They called him the Ghost Horse of the Plains.

The cowboys and *vaqueros* had other names. To them he was the Phantom Horse or the White King of the Prairies. Often they saw him flying across the distance like a white bird. At night the ranchers heard his proud whinny outside their own corrals. Their range horses stomped and whinnied back, so they knew they weren't 'hearing things.' They could tell by his perfect hoof-prints when he had visited their watering troughs and salt licks.

They all wanted to rope him and to break him in. Many a young cowhand lay awake in his bunk, thinking of the mustang. He'd lie there thinking of how he'd throw the lasso, how he'd buy a saddle trimmed with silver and blue turquoise, and how the girls would stare when he rode the proud beauty into town. But that was as far as he ever got.

Perhaps it was cruel for men to dream of capturing the free King of the Prairies. But in those days men needed horses. They needed fast, tough ponies who could ride the open range after runaway cattle. Race horses were fast, but they were frail. And farm horses were tough, but they were slow. The wild mustangs who had lived on the prairies for three hundred years were just right. They had Arab blood in their veins. The white stallion, of course, was the best of the mustangs.

As years passed the white horse was seen more and more often. Perhaps he grew careless. A *vaquero* learned his favorite watering hole. Here he hid one spring night, waiting for his prize.

At dawn his hopes came true. The proud stallion picked his way to the edge of the brook and dipped his muzzle into the water. As quietly as a cat the Mexican poised his lasso. When the mustang raised his head, the noose slipped over his neck.

With a wild leap the mustang cleared the stream and yanked the rope out of the cowboy's hand. Once more he was free! But the noose remained around his throat. After that whenever he was seen the loose end of the lariat trailed behind him.

This taught him a lesson. He became more clever than ever at escaping his captors. It made the men of the West more anxious to capture him, however.

A group of Oklahoma cowboys thought they had him trapped in a large circular valley. At every mile they stationed a fresh rider on a swift race horse. Let the King try to run away from them this time!

But when the chase started, the mustang paced around the circle and out into the hills as calmly as a pony in a riding ring. The galloping race horses were unable to come near him.

At last a Canadian hunter heard the story of the white mustang. He had hunted wolf and deer and bear. He had never failed to catch his game. He boasted that he could take the King of the Prairies, too.

The White Mustang

He knew that mere speed and strength would never succeed. It took brains and patience. He boasted that he had brains and patience to spare.

He bought a ranch in the *Llana Estacada*. He knew the stallion was at home in this country. Out on the open range he built a box stall, as strong as a bank vault and large enough for two horses.

He lined the stall with the sweetest hay and clover he could find. He filled the feed trough with oats. He found the loveliest young mare in the whole country. She was a beautiful thing, slim and brown, with large deep blue eyes and a honey-colored mane. He led her into the stall and fastened her halter to an iron ring.

The door was fitted with a trap lock. Once the stallion stepped across the threshold, the heavy oaken gate would fall and the iron bolts would clamp shut.

His preparations complete, the hunter went back to his cabin to wait. He sat on his porch with a pair of powerful field glasses, watching the stall.

Sure enough! About sundown he heard the high, eager whinny of the mare. Another answered. The white stallion himself appeared on the horizon, pacing daintily toward the new corral. The mustang paused outside to sniff the air. He danced around the prairie, looking into clumps of sagebrush to make sure that no two-footed man was near. Then, when he was satisfied that all was well, he slipped into the stall.

Clang! The heavy gate fell. The bolts clamped shut. The Prairie King had been taken!

The hunter shouted for joy. He wanted to claim his prize then and there. But he decided to wait. It would be dangerous to face the angry stallion right now. Furthermore the stall was strong. In the morning the wild horse would still be there.

So the hunter went to bed and dreamed of the riches and the glory he would gain from his wonderful white steed.

In the morning, however, the hunter's dream turned to dust. Where the stall had been, there was now a heap of splintered wood. The iron bolts had been kicked into crumpled shapes. Not a single stout oaken beam remained.

And over the hill, pacing off toward the mountains, were the White Stallion and the lovely young mare.

The mysterious King of the Prairies and his brown companion were never seen again by human eye. Where they went, no one knows.

Some years later, cowhands noticed that the best mustangs taken in the roundups belonged to a new breed. These were faster and tougher than any captured before. When broken, they made wonderful ponies for the range and the rodeo. All of them were creamy white, with big patches of brown. Because of these spots the cattlemen called them *pintos*, or 'painted' ponies.

Of course, no one can prove it, but everyone knows that the *pintos* were the children of the White Stallion and his lovely brown mare.

The Golden Cities of Cibola

23

DON JUAN DE ESCOBAR and his pretty bride, Maria, rode with the gay company through the streets of Compostela. All the knights and noblemen of Mexico had gathered with their ladies. Some of them were riding north with Coronado to seek the gold of the wonderful cities of Cibola, in what is now New Mexico. Others had come to wish them luck.

What a sight it was! The three hundred Spanish knights rode in their finest armor, breastplates and lances flashing in the sun. On their helmets they wore the colors of their ladies. Don Juan's were silver and blue in honor of Maria.

'Farewell, my lovely one,' he whispered to her as the trumpet sounded. 'Within the year I shall return to lay at your feet such treasures as you have never dreamed. You shall have pearls and rubies to wear at your throat, and dresses of cloth of gold. Never doubt it. Remember the words of Da Vaca.'

Leaning down from his saddle, he kissed his young wife.

The trumpet sounded again, the leader Coronado lifted his sword. '*Dios y Santiago!*' he shouted. 'God and Saint James! He who lives, shall see!' Then off rode the procession, until it disappeared into the northern desert in a cloud of dust.

Back to Mexico City went Maria, to think happily of the day when her Juan should return, to lay his treasures at her feet. She had heard often enough of the riches promised by Da Vaca.

Two years ago a strange, weary creature had been brought to Mexico City by a party of soldiers. They had met him in the desert. He seemed at first to be an Indian, half dead with thirst. But he was no Indian. He was a Spaniard with a wonderful story to tell.

He said he had been shipwrecked off the coast of Florida, near the spot where Ponce de Leon had sought the Fountain of Youth. For years he had wandered through the wilds of America, sometimes cared for by the Indians. From them he had learned of a country so rich that its houses and walls were built of pure gold! No one could imagine the riches that were hidden there.

Then, miracles of miracles! On his wanderings through the desert he had seen it himself. From a hilltop he had seen shimmering in the distance the seven cities, the wonderful cities of Cibola. Every word he had heard was true. The walls gleamed in the setting sun, glittering with jewels.

When he had told his story, no one in Mexico could rest until the cities had been found. Francisco Coronado, then a favorite with the governor, had been given permission to ride north until he found them. He gathered three hundred of the bravest young knights, Juan de Escobar among them.

While Maria sat dreaming in her garden, Juan and his fel-

lows rode north. Over mountains and deserts they plodded, stopping at night to make camp beside a river or in a canyon. Coronado's party was like a small army. In addition to the knights, there were a thousand Indians to act as guides and servants and a thousand pack-horses to carry supplies.

As they moved slowly northward their fine silks faded in the hot sun, their plumes drooped, and their soft leather boots were scratched by thorns. Little they cared, however. Ahead of them lay the promised treasure house which they were to take for Spain.

Toward the end of the journey Marcos de Nizza, who had been sent ahead, raced back to the company. He, too, had seen the golden cities. In the rays of the rising sun their towers had glistened.

Without stopping to rest or to eat, the party pushed on. At the top of a hill they stopped. Before them lay the cities of Cibola. The golden cities of Cibola?

All their dreams and hopes were crushed. Under the bright light of noon huddled seven little mud pueblos. These were no golden cities. These were merely poor Indian villages.

Weary and disappointed as they were, the Spaniards rode down the valley to Hawikuh, the first of the pueblos. The Indians saw them coming and gathered to meet their visitors. Before the town they drew a line of cornmeal. This was a sign that they did not welcome the white man. If he chose to cross it, he must first conquer its defenders.

Coronado, angry at his failure to find gold, urged his men onward. Soon the weary Spaniards had a fight on their hands. This was what they had crossed the mountains and the deserts to find.

After the battle, the Mexican nobles had to decide what to

The Golden Cities of Cibola

do. They had conquered Cibola, but they did not dare to return to the governor without any treasure. They might be thrown into prison for their pains. Surely they would be the laughing-stock of all New Spain.

As they wondered what to do next, an Indian came into their camp. He told them of another country, the Gran Quivira, even richer than the cities they had hoped to find. Exactly where it was, he didn't know. Sometimes he pointed to the northwest, sometimes to the southwest. But he insisted that the Gran Quivira could be found.

No one could imagine the wealth of this magnificent place. It was like a second Garden of Eden. It lay on a broad river, six miles wide. The fish that swam here were as large as horses. Great canoes floated on the surface, each with its awning of cloth of gold. Golden eagles were carved on the prow. Forty slaves manned the oars of each canoe.

Tartarrax, the king of Gran Quivira, lived a life of royal ease. Each afternoon he took his nap on a bed of roses in a beautiful garden. He lay under a tree whose branches were hung with little golden bells. These jingled softly in the warm breeze and lulled him to sleep. Gold and silver dishes covered his table. When he prayed to the Queen of Heaven, he fingered a cross of gold and precious jewels.

All these wonders brought new hope to Juan de Escobar. He wrote a long letter to Maria, telling her of the uncounted wealth he would soon be bringing home with him.

For a year the Spanish soldiers explored the West. Coronado made a camp at the village of Tiguex. From this central point he sent out exploring parties, one in one direction, one in another.

Don Juan was sent first to the West. Through the painted desert and the petrified forest they made their way until they came to a great canyon, the Grand Canyon of the Colorado — but they found no sign of King Tartarrax and his tree with the golden bells. Other parties meanwhile had marched through the bare prairies of the Northeast, as far as Nebraska. These, too, returned without any gold.

Some of the men died of hunger and thirst, others were killed in battle with Indians. Of the brave three hundred, very few were left. Coronado knew that soon he would have to return to Mexico. As a last chance he picked twenty of his best men and sent them to explore the Rio Grande Valley. Perhaps here they would find their long-sought treasure.

Don Juan de Escobar was one of the twenty. Always in his thoughts was Maria, his bride, who waited in her garden at home. For her he should succeed. He knew it.

His party traveled south for several days. Soon they reached the fearful country which the Indians call 'the journey of death.' Rocky cliffs forced them to leave the river valley for the desert where sagebrush and cactus were the only living things.

As the little party slept in its camp the third night, three horses broke away from the others and wandered into the desert to find water. One of these belonged to Escobar. Without his horse an explorer was lost. So Escobar and his two companions set out to find their steeds. By nightfall of the next day they had not returned. The desert had swallowed them alive.

Sadly their fellows returned to Coronado. The great leader gathered together his followers and started back to Mexico. His trip had been a failure.

News of Coronado's return reached the capital of New Spain long before he did. Some Mexican Indians had seen his little army and raced to tell the governor of his coming.

The Golden Cities of Cibola

Not knowing that he was worn out and empty-handed, the gentlefolk of the city rode to Compostela to greet him. Their party was as gay as that which had cheered the explorers on their way.

Maria, of course, dressed in her prettiest gown, rode to Compostela to meet her husband. It had been more than two years since she had seen him. Little she cared whether or not he brought treasure. All she wanted to see was her Juan.

Eagerly she looked for him in the group of ragged, wretched soldiers. She called his name up and down their lines without an answer. No one dared to tell her what had happened. At last one of Escobar's friends, heart-broken to see Maria's disappointment, told her a lie.

'Don Juan is in another party,' he said. 'Some of the men rode south to Mexico City itself. You must have missed him.'

Maria hurried back to her home. But Juan, of course, was not there. A few of the explorers had reached the city ahead of her. They, too, were afraid to tell her the truth.

'Perhaps he has gone to your parents' home to find you,' they lied. 'Go there. He is surely waiting for you.'

Once again Maria raced off. But again she did not find her husband. Finally she learned the truth. Don Juan de Escobar had been lost in the desert. He had never returned. Heart-broken, Maria returned to Mexico City. She shut herself up in her home and refused to see anyone. Day after day she sat in her garden, thinking about her lost husband.

And then, in the fall of the year, soldiers appeared at her gate. Half carrying, half leading, they brought with them a thin, starving creature, too weak to walk by himself. Maria ordered her servant to feed the poor wretch. She herself could not bear to look upon him.

In a moment the servant returned to the garden. 'Come, Dona Maria, come at once,' he insisted. 'It is Don Juan.'

It was indeed Don Juan de Escobar. By a miracle he had kept himself alive in the desert, drinking the milk of the cactus. Indians had found him at a little spring and had taken him prisoner. Somehow or other he had escaped, and made his way home.

When he had been given food and rest and had told his story, he sat beside his happy wife in the garden. 'I have brought you no treasure,' he said sadly. 'The wealth of Cibola, the golden bells of Quivira — none of these can I lay at your feet, Maria.'

'What do I care about the golden bells of Quivira?' she laughed gaily. 'Come, see the treasure that I have for you. Perhaps you will think it even better than the gold of your seven cities.'

She ran into the house and soon returned. 'Here is our treasure,' she said. To Juan the treasure she brought was far greater than any he had hoped for. By the hand she led a tiny boy, the youngest Don Juan de Escobar.

Pecos Bill

24

GRANDY COYOTE was out for his afternoon run along the bank of the Pecos River. Grandy was the honored grandfather and chief wise man of all the coyotes of Texas. As he loped along, snuffing in the sagebrush, the sharp warning smell of human struck his nose. Ordinarily that was the signal for a smart coyote to head in the opposite direction. But Grandy didn't turn away. He had heard a baby cry from the direction of the smell. He went to see what was up.

In a clump of sagebrush lay a little boy about two years old. There were no grown-up humans near-by. The child must have fallen out of a prairie schooner as it jounced up the bank. The pioneers had families so large that one child could easily be lost without being missed for several days.

Grandy took a fancy to little Crop Ear, as he called the baby. He picked him up and trotted him home to the pack. He fed him and played with him until his foundling was as happy as any coyote cub.

As the years went on Grandy adopted Crop Ear as his own

and favorite son. He taught him all the tricks of the desert and the prairie. Crop Ear learned to sit on his haunches and bay at the moon. He ran on four legs as did the other cubs. He hunted with the pack. He learned the animal language and the bird language. He could speak with any living creature, except man, in his own tongue.

In order to protect his foster child, Grandy called a council of all the animals of the plains. From each one he asked a pledge that Crop Ear would not be injured. For he knew that the boy was at a disadvantage. All but the rattlesnake and the wowser agreed.

These two were the most bitter of all man's natural enemies. They were famous for their bad dispositions. The wowser was a cross between a mountain lion and a grizzly bear and had all the meanness and ill temper of both.

Fortunately Crop Ear soon learned to stay away from them. He listened for their warnings — the rattle of the snake and the snarl of the wowser — and so grew up to be a strong young coyote-man without mishap.

The only thing that Grandy refused to teach the boy was the fact that he was a human. No member of the tribe was allowed to tell Crop Ear the story of his adoption. So far as he knew, he was a coyote cub and had been born into the pack.

He might have gone through life without learning the truth if it hadn't been for a cowboy named Chuck. Chuck was riding the range when he saw a strange wild creature. It certainly looked like a man. But when it saw Chuck and his pony it slunk off into the bushes on all fours, just like a coyote. The cowpuncher tried to get a closer view. After a day of tempting it with bits of jerked beef from his lunch, he was able to pat its ugly matted hair.

He tried to talk to it in every language he could think of. He spoke in cowpuncher American, high-brow English, and *vaquero* Spanish. The creature sat on its haunches listening with interest. It seemed unable to understand. But Chuck could see that it was trying to recall something to mind. At last its face lit up with a smile. Out gushed a torrent of words such as 'Ga-ga. Ma-ma. Wa-wa.' Baby talk!

Yes, Crop Ear was talking baby talk. It was the only human speech he had known before his life with the coyotes. Naturally, when he started to speak like a human again, he started in where he had left off.

'Well, tan my hide!' exclaimed Chuck. He 'goo-gooed' back in great style. For several hours the two men stood there, gurgling and calling each other 'itsy-bitsy,' like babies in nursery school.

Then Chuck began to experiment. He branched out into kindergarten and first-grade language. Crop Ear had learned the secret of imitating from a mockingbird. He caught on quickly. By sundown he had mastered the art of speaking cultured English as well as any lecturer.

Then the real conversation began. Crop Ear told Chuck about his life with the coyotes. Chuck told him about the outside world. They talked for several days.

At noon on the fourth day, Chuck noticed that Crop Ear had a blue mark on his left arm. He looked at it carefully. It was a five-pointed star, just like the one on his own arm.

'Yippee, ti-yi!' he yelled. 'If you aren't my brother Bill, the one that fell out of the wagon on the Pecos bank! We always wondered what had become of you.'

Crop Ear asked Chuck to explain this outburst. Chuck then told him all about his family. Their mother had had trouble telling her children from the neighbors'. So she had them all tattooed with blue stars on their left arms. Whenever she saw a blue star, she knew the child was hers.

Although Bill, as he called himself now, hated to leave his dear friends the coyotes, he knew it was his duty to return to the human race. Chuck bought him an outfit of clothes and took him to his own ranch, the I.X.L.

The cow hands were amazed at their strange new mate. They were even more amazed at the things he could do. He never had to rope a cow. He talked to her politely in her own language. When the boys raced their ponies up and down the range, Bill took off his shoes and loped along on all fours. Even so he outran the fastest mustangs.

Soon he was elected the boss of the ranch. He took to the life as a duck takes to water. Before long he was making improvements.

Before Bill came to the I.X.L., a cowboy's life was very easy. The herds looked after themselves. Nobody cared whether or not they wandered off. All the hands had to do was to sit in the bunkhouse. They played cards and rolled cigarettes all day long. If they wanted exercise they raced their ponies. On Saturday nights they roared into the nearest village and shot it up.

Once in a long while a steer had to be roped and butchered for food. The method of roping was very poor. A cowboy laid out a loop of rope on the ground and hid behind a tree. When a steer stepped into the loop, the man pulled his end of the rope. Sometimes he had to stand all day before a steer would step in.

Bill changed all this. He invented the lasso. He practiced whirling it around his head and slinging the loop over the steers' necks. He became so clever at it he could lasso an owl out of the top of a tree while his broncho was galloping at full speed. Then he taught this trick to the I.X.L. boys.

He thought it was wasteful to allow the cattle to wander off into the hills without any mark of ownership. The star on his arm gave him an idea. He had Bean Hole, the cook, bend an iron into the shape of I.X.L. Then he heated it over the kitchen stove until it glowed like a ruby. He held it against the flank of a steer until the hair burned off. When the scar healed no one could mistake his animal. He had invented branding.

His next invention was the roundup. Every spring and every fall he had the boys ride out to the range and bring in all the cattle marked with his brand. It was simpler this way to keep track of the herd.

As you can see, the cowboys had no time left for their former lazy life. Bill kept them busy. Some of them resented all the work. They grew cross and tired and complained that they had no fun any more. So Bill had to scratch his head and think up another invention. This one was the rodeo. After every roundup he held a big party. Every hand in the outfit had a chance to show off. This made them all completely happy.

A few gangs of cowpunchers refused to take Bill's new method of cowpunching. They said the life was too hard. They much preferred their old lazy habits of playing cards and being tough and shooting up the towns on Saturday nights.

The worst of these gangs was the Devil's Cavalry. It had a hideout in a canyon called Hell's Gate Gulch. Old Satan was the name of the leader. He claimed that Bill was a sissy and that no coyote could tell him what to do. In defiance he rode into the town of Dallas and shot all the glass out of the windows. Furthermore he took to stealing cattle. He roped several of Bill's prize bulls and sold them to an Indian.

This made Bill mad. He vowed to make Old Satan listen to reason. He knew it would be a rough trip to Hell's Gate Gulch. He didn't want his boys to be hurt, so he went alone.

It was to be more of a trip than he bargained for. He had gone not more than a day's journey when he met his old enemy Granddaddy Rattler. The big old snake was coiled in the middle of his road. It sprang at his horse. The pony lunged aside and fell, breaking his leg. Immediately Bill was on his feet and grasped the snake.

The rattler was a strong fellow. But he was not strong enough for Pecos Bill. After an hour's terrible battle, the cowman had his enemy by the throat.

'Are you going to obey me?' roared Bill.

The snake gagged and struggled for breath. 'Y-yes, sir,' he said meekly.

'That's better,' said the cowpuncher, cooling off a little. 'Now wrap yourself around my arm and come along.'

With the snake coiled around his arm, Bill loped off down the road, on all fours this time. He'd had to shoot his horse.

At the end of the second day's journey Bill heard a snarl above his head. He looked up just in time to see the King of the Wowsers leaping down on top of him from an overhanging cliff. He jumped aside, but now he had another fight on his hands. Quickly the snake unwound itself and slid to the side of the road. The fight with the wowser was even worse than the fight with the snake. But at the end, Pecos Bill had his enemy's promise to come along meekly. Bill saddled him and bridled him. Then when the snake had coiled itself around his arm again, he set out riding the wowser.

At last the strange party came to Hell's Gate Gulch. Old

Yankee Doodle's Cousins

Satan and the Devil's Cavalry were having a merry time. They were sitting around their campfire roaring and bragging. They were telling all the terrible things they would do to Pecos Bill when they met him.

Bill moved up quietly behind them. With a terrible yell he stepped out. In that yell were all the animal and bird screams and roars and bellows he had learned as a cub among the coyotes. The wowser gave his own terrifying howl. The rattler shook his rattles.

The Devil's Cavalry were so frightened they couldn't move. They turned as white as a salt lick. Their knees shook so that their six-guns and cutlasses clinked like Christmas-tree ornaments in a strong wind.

Bill strode into the midst of the party. 'Who's the boss of this outfit?' he growled.

Poor Old Satan fainted on the ground. When he came to he looked up timidly and murmured, 'I was, but you be now.'

That was all there was to it. Bill lassoed the gang together and carried them back to I.X.L., where he taught them to be good, modern cowpunchers. The rattler and the wowser came along too, as pets.

One summer, Bill had trouble with the weather. First came a drought. The range grass dried up and the cattle had nothing to eat. All the springs and rivers dried up. Bill dug a canal, hoping that this would solve his problem. It was a lovely canal, but no water flowed into it. Then Bill took his lasso and roped a ten-mile piece of the Rio Grande River. This was enough to last the ranch a day. Every morning before breakfast Bill had to rope himself another length.

As though this were not bad enough, the sky grew green. From the mountains came the wild roar of a tornado. The boys divided the cattle to keep them from stampeding. They

Pecos Bill

did their best to keep them out of the hurricane's path. It wasn't any use. The tornado headed for them whichever way they went.

To save his ranch, Bill risked his own life. He swung his lasso around his head and let fly. The noose caught the tornado and Bill was yanked up, up, up into the middle of the ugly green cloud.

The thought that a human had roped it was unbearable to the cyclone. It whipped around and around, bucked up and down, tried side-kicking and sky-walking, all the tricks of a bucking steer. Bill held on for dear life. Over plains and mountains they raced. The cyclone tried to brush him off against the Rockies. It slapped him against the walls of the Grand Canyon. It bumped his head against the sky. Still Pecos Bill kept his seat.

At last, seeing that there was no other means of shaking off its rider, the tornado headed for the Pacific Ocean and tried to rain out from under him. Bill decided he had had enough. He picked out a pleasant spot in California and jumped. The force with which he landed dug a big hole. Today this is known as Death Valley.

One of the strange things the cyclone did was almost too much for Bill. Before he threw his lasso he put two things into his pocket, a twenty-dollar gold piece and a bowie knife. With these he knew he could get along wherever the tornado landed him. As soon as he hit the earth, he felt in his pocket. The twenty-dollar gold piece had been changed into a couple of half-dollars and a plugged nickel. The bowie knife had shrunk. It was changed into a lady's pearl-handled penknife.

Pecos Bill and His Bouncing Bride

25

THERE were two loves in the life of Pecos Bill. The first was his horse Widow-Maker, a beautiful creamy white mustang. The second, was a girl, a pretty, gay creature named Slue-Foot Sue.

Widow-Maker was the wildest pony in the West. He was the son of the White Mustang. Like his father he had a proud spirit which refused to be broken. For many years cowboys and *vaqueros* had tried to capture him. At last Pecos Bill succeeded. He had a terrible time of it. For a whole week he lay beside a water hole before he could lasso the white pony. For another week he had to ride across the prairies, in and out of canyons and briar patches, before he could bring the pony to a walk. It was a wild ride indeed. But after Bill's ride on the cyclone it was nothing.

At last the white stallion gave up the struggle. Pecos patted his neck gently and spoke to him in horse language.

'I hope you will not be offended,' he began as politely as possible, 'but beauty such as yours is rare, even in this glorious state of Texas. I have no wish to break your proud spirit. I feel that together you and I would make a perfect team. Will you not be my partner at the I.X.L. Ranch?'

The horse neighed sadly. 'It must be,' he sighed. 'I must give up my freedom. But since I must, I am glad that you are the man who has conquered me. Only Pecos Bill is worthy to fix a saddle upon the son of the great White Stallion, the Ghost King of the Prairie.'

'I am deeply honored,' said Pecos Bill, touched in his heart by the compliment.

'It is rather myself who am honored,' replied the mustang, taking a brighter view of the situation.

The two of them went on for several hours saying nice things to each other. Before they were through, the pony was begging Pecos to be his master. Pecos was weeping and saying he was not fit to ride so magnificent a beast. In the end, however, Pecos Bill made two solemn promises. He would never place a bit in the pony's mouth. No other human would ever sit in his saddle.

When Bill rode back to I.X.L. with his new mount, the second promise was broken. Old Satan, the former bad man, had not completely recovered from his badness. He was jealous of Bill. When he saw the beautiful white stallion he turned green and almost burst with jealousy. One night he stole out to the corral. Quietly he slipped up beside the horse and jumped into the saddle.

Pegasus, as the horse was called, knew right away that his rider was not Pecos Bill. He lifted his four feet off the ground and bent his back into a perfect semicircle. Old Satan flew off like an arrow from a bow. He flew up into the air, above the moon, and came down with a thud on top of Pike's Peak. There he sat howling with pain and fright until the boys at I.X.L. spotted him.

Bill was angry. He knew, however, that Old Satan had had enough punishment. In his kind heart he could not allow the villain to suffer any more than he had to. So he twirled his lasso around his head, let it fly, and roped Old Satan back to the Texas ranch. The former desperado never tried to be bad again.

The cowhands were so impressed by the pony's bucking they decided to change his name. From that time on they dropped the name of Pegasus and called him Widow-Maker. It suited him better.

The story of Bill's other love, Slue-Foot Sue, is a long one. It began with the tale of the Perpetual Motion Ranch. Bill had bought a mountain from Paul Bunyan. It looked to him like a perfect mountain for a ranch. It was shaped like a cone, with smooth sides covered with grassy meadows. At the top it was always winter. At the bottom it was always summer. In between it was always spring and fall. The sun always shone on one side; the other was always in shade. The cattle could have any climate they wished.

Bill had to breed a special kind of steer for his ranch. These had two short legs on one side and two long legs on the other. By traveling in one direction around the mountain, they were able to stand up straight on the steep sides.

The novelty wore off, however, and at last Bill sold the Perpetual Motion Ranch to an English duke. The day that the I.X.L. boys moved out, the lord moved in. He brought with him trainload after trainload of fancy English things. He had featherbeds and fine china and oil paintings and real silver and linen tablecloths and silk rugs. The cowboys laughed themselves almost sick when they saw these dude things being brought to a cattle ranch.

Pecos Bill didn't laugh. He didn't even notice the fancy things. All he could see was the English duke's beautiful daughter. She was as pretty as the sun and moon combined. Her hair was silky and red. Her eyes were blue. She wore a sweeping taffeta dress and a little poke bonnet with feathers on it. She was the loveliest creature Pecos Bill had ever seen.

She was as lively and gay as she was pretty. Bill soon discovered that Slue-Foot Sue was a girl of talent. Before anyone could say 'Jack Robinson,' she changed into a cowboy suit and danced a jig to the tune of 'Get Along, Little Dogies.'

Bill soon lost all his interest in cowpunching. He spent his afternoons at the Perpetual Motion Ranch, teaching Sue to ride a broncho. Sue could ride as well as anyone, but she pretended to let him teach her. After several months of Bill's lessons, she put on a show. She jumped onto the back of a huge catfish in the Rio Grande River and rode all the way to the Gulf of Mexico, bareback. Bill was proud of her. He thought she had learned her tricks all from him.

Sue's mother was terribly upset by her daughter's behavior. She didn't care much for Bill. She was very proper. It was her fondest hope that Sue would stop being a tomboy and marry an earl or a member of Parliament.

As soon as she realized that her daughter was falling in love with a cowboy, she was nearly heart-broken. There was nothing she could do about it, however. Slue-Foot Sue was a headstrong girl who always had her own way.

At last the duchess relented. She invited Bill to tea and began to lecture him on English manners. She taught him

Pecos Bill and His Bouncing Bride

how to balance a teacup, how to bow from the waist, and how to eat scones and marmalade instead of beans and bacon. He learned quickly, and soon the duchess was pleased with him. She called him 'Colonel.'

When the boys from the I.X.L. Ranch saw what was going on they were disgusted. Here was their boss, their brave, big, cyclone-riding Pecos Bill, mooning around in love like a sick puppy. They laughed at his dude manners. They made fun of his dainty appetite. When he dressed up in his finery to call on his girl, they stood in the bunkhouse door. They simpered and raised their eyebrows and said to one another, 'La-dee-da, dearie, ain't we fine today!'

But for all their kidding they were broken-hearted. None of them had anything against Sue. They admired the way she rode a horse and played a guitar and danced a jig. But the thought of losing Bill to a woman was too much. Even worse was the thought that Bill might get married and bring a woman home to live with them. That was awful.

In spite of their teasing and the duchess's lessons, Bill asked Slue-Foot Sue to marry him. She accepted before he could back out. Her father, the lord, had always liked Bill and was terribly pleased at the match.

On his wedding day Pecos Bill shone like the sun in his new clothes. His boys were dressed in their finest chaps and boots for the occasion. Half of them were going to be grooms-men. The other half were going to be bridesmen. At first Bill asked them to be bridesmaids, but they refused. They said that was going too far.

They rode to the Perpetual Motion Ranch in a fine procession, Bill at the head on Widow-Maker. The white horse pranced and danced with excitement.

At the ranch house waited the rest of the wedding party.

The lord had sent back to England for a bishop to perform the ceremony. There stood His Eminence in his lace robes. On his one hand stood the duke in a cutaway coat. On his other hand stood the duchess in a stiff purple gown right from Paris.

Down the stairs came the bride. She was a vision of beauty. She wore a white satin dress cut in the latest fashion. It had a long lace train, but its chief glory was a bustle. A bustle was a wire contraption that fitted under the back of the dress. It made the skirt stand out and was considered very handsome in those days.

As Slue-Foot Sue danced down the steps even the cowhands forgot their sorrow. They jumped down from their horses and swept their sombreros from their heads. Pecos Bill lost his head. He leapt down from Widow-Maker and ran to meet her. 'You are lovely,' he murmured. 'I promise to grant you every wish you make.'

That was a mistake. A devilish gleam twinkled in Sue's eye. For months she had been begging Bill to let her ride Widow-Maker. Bill, of course, had always refused.

Now Sue saw her chance. Before she allowed the wedding to proceed, she demanded that Bill give her one ride on his white mustang.

'No, no!' cried Pecos Bill. Before he could stop her Sue dashed down the drive and placed her dainty foot into the stirrup. The duchess screamed. The bishop turned pale.

Widow-Maker gave an angry snort. This was the second time the promise to him had been broken. He lifted his four feet off the ground and arched his back. Up, up, up shot Slue-Foot Sue. She disappeared into the clouds.

'Catch her, catch her!' roared Bill at the boys. They spread themselves out into a wide circle. Then from the sky

Pecos Bill and His Bouncing Bride

came a scream like a siren. Down, down, down fell Sue. She hit the earth with terrible force. She landed on her bustle. The wire acted as a spring. It bounced. Up again she flew.

Up and down, up and down between the earth and sky Sue bounced like a rubber ball. Every time she fell her bustle hit first. Back she bounced. This went on for a week. When at last she came back to earth to stay, she was completely changed. She no longer loved Pecos Bill

The wedding was called off and the boys returned to the I.X.L. with their unhappy boss. For months he refused to eat. He lost interest in cowpunching. He was the unhappiest man Texas had ever seen.

At last he called his hands together and made a long speech. He told them that the days of real cowpunching were over. The prairie was being fenced off by farmers. These 'nesters,' as he called them, were ruining the land for the ranchers. He was going to sell his herd.

The I.X.L. had its last roundup. Bill gathered all the prime steers together and put them on the train for Kansas City. Then he divided the cows and calves among his boys. He himself mounted Widow-Maker and rode away.

The boys hated to see him go, but they knew how he felt. 'Nesters' or no 'nesters,' the real reason for his going was his broken heart.

None of them ever saw him again. Some of them thought he had gone back to the coyotes. Others had an idea that Slue-Foot Sue had changed her mind and that she and Bill were setting up housekeeping in some private canyon. But they never knew.

Some years later an old cowhand claimed that Bill had died. The great cowpuncher had met a dude rancher at a rodeo. The dude was dressed up in an outfit he had bought from a movie cowboy. The dude's chaps were made of doe-skin. His boots were painted with landscapes and had heels three inches high. The brim of his hat was broad enough to cover a small circus. Bill took a good look at him and died laughing.

Ol' Paul Bunyan

OL' PAUL BUNYAN, inventor, map-changer, scholar, giant, and hero — Ol' Paul Bunyan is the greatest of all Yankee Doodle's Cousins. Even Tony Beaver considered Paul his lord and master.

Most of the other heroes have disappeared. But not Paul Bunyan. He is an immortal. Like the old gods of the Greeks and the Norsemen, he lives forever. Wherever there are forests to be cut, rivers to be straightened, and lakes to be dug, there you will find his footprints and those of Babe, his big blue ox.

Although it's hard to believe, Paul Bunyan was not born in Real America, as he calls the United States. His name was at first Paul Bonjean. His father and mother were French Canadian fisherfolk from New Brunswick.

Nevertheless, Paul is the patron saint of the Real Americans. His people are lumberjacks and miners and engineers — all the people who do Big Things and have Big Thoughts. When they gather about their campfires and bunkhouse stoves, they swap stories and compare notes. Once in a while, some one of them will have a new story to tell. From the twinkle in his eye and the lilt in his voice, his listeners know that he is indeed a Real American. He has had a glimpse of Ol' Paul himself.

When cold winds blow down from Canada, when hot dust

storms sweep from the Western prairie, when the Northern Lights dance in the sky, when floods roar through the lowlands, then you know that Ol' Paul is up to his old tricks, doing Big Things in a Big Way.

How Paul Bonjean Became
Paul Bunyan

26

EVEN before he let out his first baby squall, it was obvious that Paul Bonjean was going to be a hero. He was a large baby, as babies go. Instead of the usual seven or eight pounds, *le petit* Paul weighed seventy or eighty. He was born with a long, glossy black beard and a pair of beautifully waxed and curled mustaches. Furthermore, you could see him grow.

Monsieur Bonjean, his father, nearly burst with pride. Before nightfall, however, he was worried. For the baby had drunk up all the milk that Marie, the cow, could give. The little clothes that Madame Bonjean had made were no longer of any use. The cabin bunk wouldn't hold him. Papa Bonjean wrung his hands in despair.

The neighbors did what they could to help. They gave the baby all the milk from their cows. They gave their sheets for diapers. They spread their blankets in the ox stall for him. Then they went home to bed.

Yankee Doodle's Cousins

In the morning the whole village gazed in awe at the new baby. He had grown so fast during the night that his chubby little feet and hands stuck out through the doors and windows of the ox shed. The big double sheets were stretched to the ripping point across his tummy. And he was as hungry as a bear. He doubled his little fist and banged it down on the ground, crushing to splinters several racks for drying codfish. He waved his little leg in the air, knocking down two pine trees and a retired sea captain. Something had to be done.

The first problem was food. All the cows in New Brunswick were herded together to give him milk. Several shiploads of cod-liver oil, meant for Boston, were put in storage for him. He had to have three barrels of it every day. The clothing problem was solved by a sailmaker from St. John. He cheerfully donated a pair of mainsails to be made into panties. The Ladies Aid Society offered to do the sewing. A wagon-maker gave a dozen cartwheels to be used for buttons.

Still there was no suitable place for the little fellow to sleep. No hayloft would hold him. Papa Bonjean tried to rent a field from a farmer. 'But,' objected the farmer, 'think of my crops. They will all be crushed and ruined.'

At last the problem was solved. A committee was sent to the shipyards in Maine. They found in one the half-built hull of a clipper ship. The ship was to be the largest in the China trade. As yet no decks nor masts had been put in. 'The very thing we want!' exclaimed the committee. So they bought it.

They asked the astonished shipwright to line the hold with featherbeds. Then they towed it up to the Bay of Fundy. With the aid of a large steam crane, they hoisted little Paul into his new cradle.

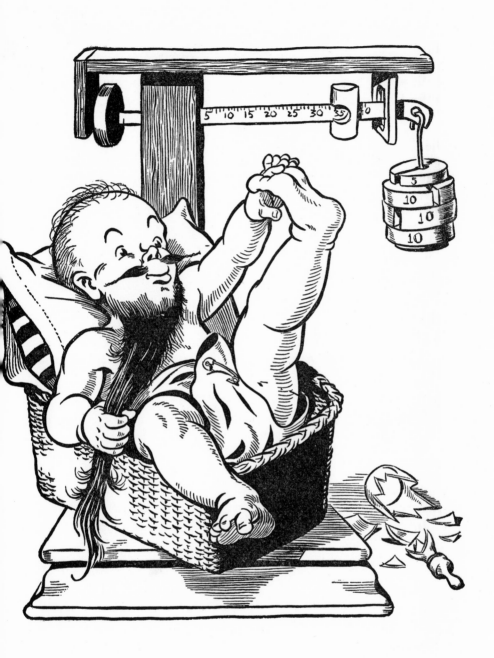

It was a perfect fit. The baby cooed and gurgled to show how happy he was, and soon fell asleep. The gentle rocking of the sea and the slap of waves against the shore were his lullabies. He slept soundly for two weeks, with his little pink thumb nestled against the glossy black of his beard and mustaches.

Unfortunately, when the time came to give him his bottle, he would not wake up. The fishermen rowed out to his cradle and yelled at him. He slept right on. The lighthouse keeper sounded the fog horn. Little Paul only sighed in his sleep. What to do next? Papa Bonjean went to the mayor. The mayor went to the Provincial Governor. The Provincial Governor went to the Governor General. He had a bright idea. He knew that part of the British Navy was stationed off the coast of Nova Scotia. So he wrote to the Admiral of the Fleet. The Admiral was very fond of children and agreed to help.

He ordered the fleet into the Bay of Fundy. He lined up the ships in battle formation opposite Paul's cradle. Then at a given signal they fired their cannon over the baby's head.

That woke him up! It frightened him, too! He opened his little mouth and screamed '*Maman!*' which is French for 'Mama!' His scream was heard in Boston by the Coast Guard Listening Station. Thinking that the whole North Atlantic fishing fleet must be in trouble, the Coast Guard sent out all its ships to see what was wrong.

Furthermore, the child trembled so in his fright that his cradle rocked from side to side, kicking up waves seventy-five feet high. Even after all these years, the water has not calmed down completely. In some places in the Bay of Fundy the tides are still fifty feet or more.

In spite of difficulties which you can well imagine, little

How Paul Bonjean Became Paul Bunyan

Paul grew up. His childhood was a happy one. His parents adored him and he loved them in return. But something bothered him. His clear blue eyes grew dreamy. His thoughts wandered into far places. He seemed to know that some great task lay ahead of him. But what it was, he couldn't tell.

He went to school with other children. He was extremely bright for his age. Even so he had his troubles. In penmanship, for instance, he could write only one letter on a page. His geography book was so large it had to be carried by an ox team. Once in a careless moment he sat on his lunch box. When he opened it later, he found the first of his many inventions — hamburger!

He had soon learned all that school could teach him. Although he loved to read, he knew that he must learn other things. He had to find out what it was he had to do in life.

Papa Bonjean suggested that he try fishing. For a year young Paul worked with nets and ships. He was a great help to his father. Every morning at sunrise, he towed a pair of three-masted schooners out into the fishing banks of the Atlantic Ocean. Before breakfast he waded back to the docks, a schooner tucked under each arm. Their holds were jammed with cod and haddock. Fishing was easy, but it didn't satisfy him. It was too easy. Surely this was not the great work he had to do!

Next he tried hunting and trapping. He went up into the Canadian woods to learn from the Indian guides. They taught him to follow the tracks of animals, of moose and bear and caribou. He became so clever at this his teachers were amazed. Once he found the body of a dead moose. From the antlers he judged it to be fifteen years old. Nevertheless, he set out to follow the big fellow's tracks — just for fun. He traced them as they grew smaller and smaller, until they became the tiny hoof-prints of a faun. He didn't give up until he had reached the moose's birthplace.

The Indians taught Paul Bonjean other tricks, especially how to shoot. In time he became a crack shot. He invented a shotgun with seventy-six barrels to make shooting more interesting. At first it was impossible to sight down all the barrels at once. But Paul's inventive genius helped him out. He rigged up a system of mirrors. The first time he tried out the gun with the mirrors he brought down seventy-six duck.

On one occasion Paul Bonjean almost lost confidence in himself. He was traveling through the forest at twilight. Far up ahead he saw the head of a deer peek out from behind a thicket. Quickly Paul dropped to his knee and aimed his gun, a single-barreled rifle, between the deer's eyes. Bang! went the gun. Pouf! The deer vanished. Paul supposed that it had dropped dead out of sight.

But, no! As he straightened up, the little head popped back into sight from behind the thicket. It was very much alive. '*Parbleu!*' muttered Paul in French Canadian, '*ce n'est pas possible!* — It can't be true. I've never missed before.'

Again he dropped to his knee, drew his bead, and pulled the trigger. Bang! went the gun. Pouf! The deer vanished. 'Ha!' sighed Paul. He felt better for a moment. Then the deer's head popped back into place again, very much alive.

This time Paul lost his temper. He used all the French Canadian cuss words he knew. Once more he aimed and fired. For the third time the deer's head disappeared and popped back into place. Now Paul was really angry. He had missed three times in a row.

'*Nom d'un nom!*' he swore. 'I'll hit that deer yet.' And

with that he started firing one shot after another. His fire sounded like that of a machine gun.

At last he had used up all his ammunition save one shot. He had fired twenty-seven times. And twenty-seven times the little deer's head had popped back into view. He gritted his teeth, took careful aim, fired. The deer vanished. Paul held his breath.

The twenty-eighth shot had done the trick. Even so, that was a bad record. He decided to have his eyes examined.

When finally he reached the thicket where his game lay, Paul Bonjean slapped his thigh and roared with laughter. '*Ho! Ho! Ho!*' he shrieked, '*c'est à rire!*' For there, instead of one deer, lay twenty-eight, each of them shot squarely between the eyes.

As great a hunter as he was, Paul was not satisfied that hunting was to be his life-work. Something inside kept urging him on to different fields. He tried one thing after another. Nothing was right. At last the desire to find Something Big to do in a Big Way got to be too much. He became cross and sulky. He wouldn't eat his dinner, not even when his mother fixed his favorite dish — a roasted moose stuffed with wild boar and a dozen wild turkeys.

He had to get away from things. So with a pack of books and provisions on his back, his rifle over his shoulder, he trudged north into the wilderness of Labrador. He was so absent-minded he stepped across the St. Lawrence River without noticing. On and on he went. At last he found a cave big enough for him, on the coast. Here he settled for the winter.

All winter long he stayed there. He left the cave only to fish and to hunt for food. The rest of the time he lay by his fire, reading and dreaming and trying to figure out just what his life-work was meant to be. He became so interested in his problem that he didn't notice the strange and wonderful snow that was falling on the world. Outside everything was hushed. Forests and thickets, fields and trails, all were being covered with a bright blue blanket. It glistened and sparkled like ground sapphires. It was as blue as Paul's eyes.

Unaware of the miracle, Paul lay dreaming in his cave. Suddenly a great noise made him wake up. He heard the thunder of snow slipping off the roof of his cave. With a rumble and a splash a heavy object tumbled over the cliff and fell into the ocean. Paul rushed out to see what it could be.

Sticking up from the cold black water were the horns and the head of a baby ox. The newborn calf lay still among the icebergs. For a moment Paul thought it was frozen or drowned. He dashed into the sea to pull it out. But it was heavy, much heavier than an ordinary calf. He had to struggle before he could lug it onto the shore and into the warmth of his cave.

When he had finally laid it down before the fire and covered it with his blankets, he had a chance to admire it. The baby ox had bright blue hair the color of the strange snow. It was a big fellow, as big as Paul himself.

'*Ah, Bébé!*' he murmured as he stroked its baby head. At that it opened its big blue eyes, and feebly it licked his face with its big pink tongue. For days and nights Paul nursed the little calf back to health. What a remarkable beast he was! Paul himself had to go hungry, for *Bébé* ate everything in sight.

He was strong — fifty times as strong as any full-grown ox should be. He was playful. He loved to play hide and seek. He liked to lie down in the blue snow, which blended perfectly with his hide. His horns stuck up like black trees.

How Paul Bonjean Became Paul Bunyan

Then Paul would wander about calling, '*Bébé, Bébé*, where are you?' And at last *Bébé*, who had been lying in plain sight all the time, would jump up and charge at the big lumberjack.

When spring came, the lovely blue snow began to melt. As the sap began to stir in the trees, Paul's problem began to stir in his mind. Somehow or other, he began to feel that he was about to solve it. Night after night he dreamt the same dream. When he got up in the morning it was gone. All that he could remember was that it had something to do with Real America.

He decided to go to Real America. Perhaps he could find there the kind of work he was meant to do. One morning he packed a little lunch and called *Bébé*. Together they set out. By evening they had reached the border. Off ahead of them stretched the state of Maine, with its miles of pine woods. As far as the eye could see there were trees, nothing but trees.

Bébé romped on ahead. When a hundred-year-old pine got in his way, he kicked it impatiently with his foot. It snapped under the force of the blow and fell crashing to the forest floor.

And then Paul knew what it was he had to do in life. He had to go to Real America and invent logging. It was his job to cut down all those trees and to make room for all the Real Americans who were coming to plant farms and build cities.

He stepped proudly across the border. He started to call, '*Holà, Bébé!*' in French Canadian. But the words wouldn't come. Instead he heard himself shouting a new language — 'Hey, Babe!'

He stopped in amazement. He pinched himself all over. He discovered that he was a New Man.

Yankee Doodle's Cousins

'By the holy old mackinaw!' he said, and he slapped his knee. 'By the great horn spoon! I'm a Real American. And I'll be durned if I'm not goin' to log off this state before you can say "Jack Robinson."' With a whoop and a holler he started right in on his new job.

And that is how *Bébé* became Babe, the blue ox. And that is how *Paul Bonjean* became Yankee Doodle's greatest cousin — Paul Bunyan!

Ol' Paul's Camp on the
Big Onion River

27

WHEN Paul Bonjean crossed the border into Maine and became Paul Bunyan, history was made. Together he and Babe moved into the great pine forests and started to work. Paul swung his axe and brought down the trees. He stripped the trunks of their branches and sawed them into logs. Meanwhile, Babe uprooted the stumps. The blue ox dragged his master's logs onto the ice of the frozen rivers. When the thaw came in the spring, Paul himself drove them to the sawmills and shipyards on the coast.

How the shipwrights loved to see him riding down the rapids! He spun the logs under his nimble feet, bringing masts and beams for the clippers. He was a fine figure of a man in those far-off days. His eyebrows and mustaches were as glossy and black as his beard. They ended in fine curls. To set off his natural beauty he liked to wear gay clothes. His hunting cap was wine red, his muffler as yellow as corn.

He wore a lumberjack coat with big orange and purple checks, and pants of tan with quiet gray stripes and a few crimson dots and crosses. Under his black boots he wore brilliant green woollen socks. He wore mittens of a plum-colored pattern on a background of white. No wonder he dazzled the villagers in the seacoast towns.

Before long Paul's business was too big for one man to handle. He had worked so hard that the forests of Maine had been cut over. He needed new helpers and new woods. So he invented loggers and logging camps.

Taking his loggers on his back, and hitching Babe to the bunkhouses of his new camps, he started west. He tried one place after another. First he put the camps down in one likely spot. The trees were tall. The snow was hard. Everything seemed perfect. By spring the river was piled high with logs. When the thaw came, the men started to drive the logs downstream. They drove and drove without getting anywhere. Three times they passed cut-over forests and well built logging camps. The third time one of the boys recognized his own bunkhouse. The camp was Paul's. It was then they discovered that the river ran in a perfect circle. They had driven past their own camp three times. With no outlet, they could never get their logs to the sea. So Paul had to try again.

He had trouble finding a good location. One river, which had a fine stand of trees, was full of boiling water. When the boys tried to spin the logs, the calks were scalded off their boats.

At last Paul found the right spot. It had its disadvantages, to be sure. But the great Bunyan could see that it might be made into an ideal camp. The river wound slowly through a rich valley. It was wide enough for two log drives at once.

Ol' Paul's Camp on the Big Onion River

The pine woods on either side were full of huge old trees. To make the boys happy, off to the north rose the Big Rock Candy Mountain. Its crystal sides shone in the sun. From its ravines gushed many lemonade springs and soda fountains. What a spot for a camp!

At first the only trouble seemed to be the smell of onion. The meadows were full of wild onions. The forests were full of them, too. When the boys started out to the woods, the biting odor made them cry. Blinded by his tears, one of them tried to chop down Paul's leg. He thought it was a giant tree.

This was discouraging. But Bunyan didn't give up. Word came that the garlic crop in Italy had failed. The Italian people were starving. Paul lost no time. He put the boys to work, harvested the onions, and sent them as a present to the King of Italy.

There were other disadvantages. The climate was bad for coughs and colds. The loggers sniffled and sneezed. However, Paul discovered that Lucy, the camp cow, liked to graze in the pine woods. Her milk was so strong of balsam that it tasted like cough syrup. He made the boys drink a glass each morning. Soon they were cured.

You can see that the great lumberjack was not easily discouraged. He was a tough one! Although the loggers were little men compared to him, they were tough, too! At first he hired only Scandinavians, Swedes and Norwegians. They were good workers. Paul liked the music of their names. They all had names like Lars Larsen, Pete Peterson, Jens Jensen, Eric Ericson, and Hans Hanson. One fine day, however, Paul hired a red-headed fellow who said his name was Murph Murphyson. He was a great woodsman. But in time the truth came out. His real name was Pat Murphy and he was Irish. The discovery nearly broke the heart of Paul Bunyan, who loved honesty above everything. He decided that it was better to have honest boys than to have all Swedes.

Among the most famous of his crew were Jim Liverpool and Shot Gunderson. Jim was an agile little Englishman. He could jump higher and farther than anyone his size. He could jump across the Mississippi in three jumps. Shot was an expert at spinning logs. He could walk out into the center of a running river on a log. Then he churned the water so fast that he could run ashore on the bubbles.

Big Ole was the blacksmith. It was his job to make shoes for Babe, the blue ox. When he carried a pair of these shoes in his hand, he sank two feet into solid rock at each step. The job for which he became most famous, however, was that of hole-puncher. After the doughnuts had been shaped out of sourdough, Big Ole placed them on his anvil and punched in the holes.

Another famous member of the crew was Brimstone Bill, who looked after Babe. No one was able to control the blue ox except Paul and Bill. It was Bill who hitched Babe to the crooked logging roads and straightened them out. His only fault was his language. He swore so much that one day he set the stables on fire. The other boys had to use a fire extinguisher to put out his cussing.

Feeding Paul's crew was no laughing matter. In the early years, the cookhouse was run by a master cook named Sourdough Sam. He took his name from the fact that he made everything of sourdough. This is exactly what it sounds like — sour dough. It rises as it becomes warm. As a matter of fact, it rises and rises and rises, and often explodes. Sam fed it to the loggers day and night. For breakfast he served it plain. For dessert he had Big Ole punch holes in it and called it doughnuts.

Poor old Sam! At last his weakness for sourdough got the better of him. The dough blew up. The old cook was in the kitchen at the time, and lost an arm and a leg in the tragedy.

Now that Sam was disabled, Paul had to get another cook. He sent to Quebec for his cousin, Joe Mufraw. He was a French Canadian. The *habitants* of Quebec live mostly on pea soup. So Joe threw out the left-over sourdough and fed the boys on his native dish. Once when Brimstone Bill and Babe were hauling a load of beans across the frozen lake, the ice broke under their great weight. Being a French Canadian, Joe Mufraw couldn't waste anything. He built a fire under the lake, and served the water as pea soup.

Unfortunately for Joe the boys grew tired of pea soup. You can see why. Paul sent south to Alabama for Hot Biscuit Slim. Slim was an artist. He took one look at the cookhouse and started to leave. Only when Paul promised to build a new one to suit him would he agree to stay. Slim's new building was a wonder. The dining hall was larger than Grand Central Station in New York. The tables were so long that a four-horse team was needed to haul the salt and pepper from shaker to shaker. Flunkies on roller skates dashed up and down filling the water glasses.

The kitchen was enormous. It was divided into departments. Overhead cranes carried the food from one section to the other. A special feature was the air-tight onion room, in which were stacked barrels and barrels of the fragrant vegetable.

Beyond the main kitchen stood a shack for the cooking of hotcakes or flapjacks. A small lake was dug to hold the batter. A second-hand steamboat was bought from a river captain to stir the ingredients. When the batter was properly mixed, it was poured on to the griddle. This was one of the marvels of the age. It was so large that at first there seemed to be no way of greasing it. Finally Slim hired an extra group of flunkies. He strapped sides of bacon to their feet and made them skate over the surface of the griddle.

With Hot Biscuit Slim in the kitchen, most of Paul's troubles were over. The food was so good that the men worked harder than ever. Paul himself had to spend all his time keeping books. He needed someone of his own stature who could boss the work in the woods. One fine day, almost in answer to prayer, a giant appeared at the camp. He was nearly, but not quite, as big as Paul. His name was Hels Helson, although he preferred to be called the Bull of the Woods. Some of the boys nicknamed him the Big Swede. The only Real American words he knew were 'Ay tank so!' When Paul offered him the job of foreman, he said simply 'Ay tank so!' And that was that.

At first Hels did a fine job. But, alas, his importance went to his head. He began to think he was as big as Paul. Meanwhile Paul Bunyan received an order to log off the Mountain That Stood on Its Head. He could see that the Big Swede's conceit was going to cause trouble. He decided to nip it in the bud.

Calling the Swede into his office, he explained the new job. The mountain really did stand on its head. The broad base was on top, the narrow peak at the bottom. All the trees grew straight down, with their roots above their heads. When Paul asked the Swede if he could manage the job, Hels said, 'Ay tank so,' and swaggered out of the office.

The next morning the new foreman sent the boys off to the job. They had a terrible time. They had to chop down the trees standing on their heads. They had to hang on to the

Ol' Paul's Camp on the Big Onion River

ground for dear life, lest they fall into the valley below them. What a situation! The work went slowly and more slowly, until it was obvious that it would never be finished. At last Paul took over. He loaded his seventy-six-barrel shotgun with crosscut saws, aimed it at the mountain, and fired. Lo and behold! Seventy-six trees fell off into the valley, their stumps cut clean. Time and again he fired until the mountain was cleared of timber.

Meanwhile Hels Helson sat brooding on the side-lines. He wanted to be the boss. He resented Bunyan's interference. At last he could stand it no longer. With a flying leap he landed on top of the mountain.

Paul looked up. It made him angry to see the Swede showing off in front of his boys. 'Who do you think you are — the boss of this outfit?' he bellowed.

'Ay tank so,' roared back the Swede.

That was enough. No one had ever before dared to question Bunyan's authority. He rolled up his sleeves, and spat on his hands. With a running jump he landed on top of the mountain beside his mutinous foreman.

'We'll see about that,' muttered the great logger. He drew back his arm and placed his fist on the Swede's chin. The Bull of the Woods replied in kind. Soon the two giants were fighting, tooth and nail. Never before or since has there been such a battle.

The fight went on for weeks. When at last the dust and the noise died down, the mountain was gone. Instead of the upside-down miracle, there remained only a few jagged hills. The Big Swede lay unconscious in their midst. Paul, the hero, the giant, the demi-god, stood upright, wiping the dust out of his eyes. Never again did anyone question his right to be the Boss.

247

Yankee Doodle's Cousins

When the Swede recovered from his wounds, he apologized. Paul forgave him and made him his foreman for life.

About this time, the loggers came upon a new country which they called Pine Orchard. Here the trees grew straight and tall, without any branches or bark. Furthermore, they were spaced in straight rows. It would be as easy as eating pie to log it off. In fact, it was a lumberjack's dream. They lost no time in calling Paul. He whistled to Babe, and within an hour a temporary camp had been set up, and the loggers were hard at work.

The work went smoothly. In no time the logs had been stacked in neat piles and were floating down the river. Paul had spent a week in his office keeping books on the job. His eyes were tired and his whole vigorous spirit rebelled against figures and pens and ink. If only he had a bookkeeper!

He and Babe set out for a walk to rest his eyes. Suddenly he noticed a mountain where no mountain should have been. He heard a moaning sound he had never heard before. There, sitting on a cliff with his feet in the river, was another giant. He was no lumberjack like Paul or the Swede. That was easy to see from his store-bought clothes and his high white collar. He was groaning and running his hands through his hair in despair.

'My stakes!' he groaned. 'My beautiful, beautiful stakes.'

Paul was a tender-hearted soul, and the sight of this sad creature touched him. He asked what the trouble might be.

'Alas,' said the stranger, 'I am a surveyor. Ten years I have labored, all for naught. I surveyed this country and planted stakes at every section line. Now they are gone, and all my work is lost. Alas! Alackaday!' He groaned louder than ever.

Ol' Paul's Camp on the Big Onion River

Paul, of course, had no idea what he was talking about. But he knew how sad the other fellow must be if his work was lost. He wanted to help.

'What do you mean, your stakes?' he asked gently.

The mention of his stakes simply made the giant moan more than ever. It was an hour before he could speak clearly. 'My surveyor's stakes. I marked this country off into sections. Wherever two section lines crossed, I planted a stake. There were hundreds and hundreds of them, all my life's work. And now someone has cut them down.' He wiped a tear from his eye. 'They stretched out as far as the eye could see, like an orchard of straight pine trunks.'

An orchard of straight pine trunks? Pine Orchard! The two ideas crossed Paul's mind at once. Slowly a bright red blush spread up his neck and across his face. Even his glossy black beard turned fiery red in his embarrassment. Pine Orchard, of course! Those beautiful trees his boys had logged off had not been trees at all. They belonged to this giant.

It was hard for him to do it, but Paul admitted to the giant what he had done. The latter let out a howl of anguish, and again buried his face in his hands. He wailed and wept until a terrible thunderstorm swept the whole United States east of the Mississippi. The poor fellow was beside himself.

Paul felt very bad about the whole thing. There was little he could do to make amends. He could see that his stupid mistake had ruined the stranger's whole life. Gently he and Babe led the moaning giant back to camp and put him to bed in Paul's own bunk. They fed him all the best foods Slim knew how to make. They waited on him day and night. If only he would stop weeping and tell them how they could repay him!

249

Yankee Doodle's Cousins

Weeks later, the stranger recovered a little. He sat up in the bunk and smiled a faint wan smile. He said he was sorry for all the trouble he had caused his host. But he couldn't help himself. He had spent years working on that surveying, and his job depended on them. Now he had no job. There was nothing else for him to do in life. Then he introduced himself. He said his name was John Rogers Inkslinger, surveyor, inventor, and bookkeeper by profession.

'Bookkeeper?' roared Paul with delight. 'Bookkeeper? I am certainly pleased to meet you.' He wrung Mr. Inkslinger's hand until the poor creature winced from pain. 'I've been looking for a bookkeeper. Will you do me the honor of working for me?' he bellowed.

Poor Mr. Inkslinger was startled. But the offer of a job and the tenderness with which Paul had nursed him back to health made him forget his sorrow. The big logger led him to the office and showed him the stacks of books that needed keeping. The sight of pen and ink was too much for the invalid. He grinned. He dashed for the desk and started to work happily.

The work was all that he needed to make him completely well. He soon forgave Paul for the accident at Pine Orchard. Forever after he was the chief bookkeeper in Bunyan's camp. One summer, when the ink threatened to give out, he saved nine barrels of it, simply by leaving the dots off the i's and the crosses off the t's. He was, in fact, a man after Paul's own heart.

With Johnny Inkslinger in the office, the Big Swede in the woods, and Slim in the kitchen, Paul was at last free to enjoy himself. He was free to act the way a hero ought to act. And while he carried on his great business of logging, he did Big Things in a Big Way.

How Ol' Paul Changed the Map of America

28

THE map of Real America must have been very dull in the days before Paul Bunyan changed it. No mountains, no lakes, no rivers! Nothing but plain, flat land! You could roller skate from the Atlantic to the Pacific, if you wanted to do such a thing.

Whether or not Paul intended to make any changes, we don't know. Wherever he went, however, strange and wonderful things took place.

He had a remarkable effect on the weather. When Paul was around, the weatherman lost his head and the seasons turned somersaults. There was the Hot Hot Hot Summer, for instance. It happened soon after Hot Biscuit Slim came to Onion River.

Slim told Paul about the joys of eating corn-on-the-cob. He described it so well that Paul could feel the hot butter trickling down his chin. His mouth watered. He had to

taste some. So he planted the whole state of Iowa with
sweet corn and licked his chops.

Paul never had his corn-on-the-cob, however. The weather
turned hot, hotter, hottest. The corn shot up out of the
ground like smoke from a fire. The kernels burst from their
ears and fell to the ground. Under the blazing sun, they
popped as they fell. Soon Iowa was covered four feet deep
with popcorn.

That wasn't the end of it, either. A big wind blew in
from the northeast and carried the corn to Kansas. There it
fell from the skies like a blizzard. Thousands of cattle, grazing on the Kansas fields, thought it was snow and promptly
froze to death.

Then there was the spring the Rains Came Up From China.
Paul and his boys were logging off the country around the
Cascade Mountains in Oregon. They had only started the
job when it began to rain. It didn't rain down from the skies.
It rained up from the earth. For days on end, the ground
oozed rain. Some drained off and formed the Cascade River
with its lovely waterfalls. In other places it never stopped.
It's still bubbling up in the hot springs and little geysers of
Yosemite Park. Incidentally, it was from this season that
Mount Rainier took its name.

Some years later, after Paul had returned to his Onion
River Camp, he became restless. He'd heard about the
cypress forests of Louisiana, and he wanted to see them. But
before he reached them, it began to rain again. This time the
rain fell down, all right, but it was all of a bright red color.
For sixteen days and seventeen nights the Red Rain fell.
Some of it is still running off in the Red River of Arkansas.

On this walk to Louisiana Paul got sand in his shoes. Of
course, sand isn't comfortable to walk on. So he sat down

on the Ozarks and poured out the sand into a ragged pile. This pile is known as the Kiamichi Mountains of Eastern Oklahoma.

I could go on all night telling you about Paul's special weather. There was the Year of the Hard Winter. The words froze in the air as soon as they were spoken. Several of the lumberjacks bumped into them in the dark and cut their foreheads. In the spring, when the conversations thawed out all at once, the noise was terrible.

Paul's most important work in changing the map, however, was done without any help from the weatherman. Just as in the case of the Kiamichi, he did it alone, sometimes by accident. Even Babe did some of it.

If you've ever been to North Dakota you know that there are huge tracks in the rocks. Scientists say that these are the tracks of dinosaurs. Dinosaurs were huge animals that lived in North America long before man became man. Of course, we know that they are Babe's hoof-prints.

There are many iron mines in Northern Michigan near Lake Superior. It was Paul who opened them in order to find metal for Babe's shoes. He opened a new one every time the ox needed to be shod.

You have read already about one of Paul's smaller feats. This took place when he fought the Big Swede on top of the Mountain That Stood on Its Head. After the battle, when the dust had cleared away, nothing remained of the strange mountain but a pile of broken earth. This is what we call the Bad Lands of the Dakotas.

Geography isn't a matter of maps alone. It takes in other things, such as businesses and farm products. Paul dabbled even in these. He went hunting in Canada one fine autumn morning. His little hunting dog Elmer suddenly found the track of a huge buck. Together Paul and Elmer trailed the buck down the St. Lawrence Valley, across Ontario. In Michigan Paul managed to shoot — but his shot merely wounded the animal. On and on raced the buck, the hunter after him. He plunged into the icy waters of Lake Michigan and struggled across. But the effort of swimming and the loss of blood were too much. The big buck fell dead on the opposite shore, right on the Chicago waterfront.

Paul didn't want the meat. He had a large dinner waiting for him back in Onion River. So he sold the carcass to a butcher, who cut it up and used it to start the meat-packing business, for which Chicago is famous.

The map of North America owes a great deal to a sad year in Paul's life. Babe became ill. His bright blue coat faded and grew dull. His lovely big eyes rolled unhappily. Paul and Johnny Inkslinger got down all their books on medicine and tried to cure him. Nothing did any good. At last Johnny suggested that a change in climate would help. Paul was only too glad to do anything that might cure his adored pet. Within an hour he had the bunkhouses packed and was off on his long trip west.

This time, of course, the procession moved slowly. Paul carried the bunkhouses on his shoulders and Brimstone Bill walked beside Babe, feeding him medicine and keeping cold packs on his head. It was a tiresome trip. In Colorado they stopped to rest. The Big Swede, in order to mark the trail, set up a pile of rocks. Paul helped him and stuck in a pike, or pole, in order to top it off. This has since become known as Pike's Peak.

From Colorado the party moved northwest. Paul had heard about the wonderful sulphur springs which cure all illnesses. In one corner of Wyoming he thought he heard one of these springs bubbling under ground. Here he stopped and started to dig a drinking hole for Babe. He'd gotten down about a hundred feet without striking water, when the hole dropped out from under. This surprised him so that he dropped his spade. Down, down, down it fell until it was completely lost from sight in the middle of the earth.

Paul was about to dig another hole with another spade, when he heard a rumbling and a hissing below. Whish! Like a shot out of a gun, his spade flew into the air. It was completely melted. It was carried up on a column of steam. High in the air it hung for a moment and then sank back into the hole.

Ever since that day, every hour on the hour, the spade has been shot up into the air and then has fallen back into the hole. Some years ago the Government named it Old Faithful and put Yellowstone Park around it.

The long trip over the Rockies was hard on the sick ox. By the time they reached Utah, he was unable to go any farther. His fever was high. He put out his pale tongue and feebly licked Paul's hand. His eyes looked up miserably as much as to say 'Good-bye.' Paul and Johnny were sure he was going to die.

The big lumberjack sadly dug a grave for his beloved Babe. As he dug he wept bitter salt tears. At last he was crying so hard he had to stop digging. He sat down beside the grave and let himself go. The tears gushed from his eyes.

Someone touched him on the shoulder. It was Brimstone Bill. Paul, of course, thought that Bill had come to tell him that Babe was dead. He wept more than ever. Not until a soft warm tongue licked his cheek did he realize that Babe was better. By some miracle the ox had lived through the crisis. He was still weak, but he was going to get well.

How Ol' Paul Changed the Map of America

Paul jumped up in joy. He hugged Babe and patted him and acted like a crazy man. He set off immediately for the pleasant climate of California, so that Babe could take it easy as he was growing stronger. But the grave full of salt tears was left behind. Great Salt Lake is there today, a monument to Paul's sorrow.

After a winter in California, Babe grew well and strong. Word came to Paul about the Stonewood Forests in Arizona. They were not far away, so he and Babe walked over one evening to see. The trees were as hard as rock. The wood was colored in lovely reds and yellows and browns. Altogether Paul thought it the most interesting logging country he had ever seen. He planned to bring his camp over and to start cutting right away.

Unfortunately, Babe's illness had left him with a bad case of hay fever. The dry, stone dust of the forest floor got up his nose. He sneezed. He sneezed again and again. His eyes began to run. Paul saw at once that this was no country for an animal with hay fever. So he gave up his plans and hurried back to California. Babe's sneezes had another effect, though. They raised the dust storms which blow across Oklahoma and Texas, burying farms and ranches under their white powder.

On the way back to California, Paul discovered a little river, shaded by walls of rock. The hot sandy floor of Arizona had burned his feet. The water looked cool and inviting. Paul pulled off his shoes and waded for a while. As he waded he let his pickaxe drag in the water behind him. To this day you can see the track it made. We call it the Grand Canyon of the Colorado River.

Paul Bunyan hated to hire himself out to another boss. He wanted to be the boss himself. Once, at least, he did agree to work for another man. The government needed a new bay, or sound. The President sent surveyors out to the West to find a good place. They suggested the coast of Washington. This sounded good to the President and he hired the Dan Puget Construction Company to do the work. Puget was a good man. But he was a little man, not used to doing things on Paul's scale. He worked and worked and worked. Alas, the job was too big for him.

He sent for Paul and begged him to come and help. Bunyan didn't like the idea of working for a man who couldn't do his own work properly. But he was kind-hearted. He felt sorry for Mr. Puget and agreed to his terms.

After one brief look around the country, Paul knew exactly what to do. Steam-shovels and pile-drivers were mere toys to him. He needed a glacier. He drove Babe up to Alaska, hitched him to a glacier with the sharp side down, and started back to the States.

They had hardly left Alaska before they had an accident. A pretty young schoolteacher with a pink parasol crossed the road. Most bulls go mad at the sight of the color red. Babe went mad when he saw pink. To make matters worse, the schoolmarm stopped in her tracks when she saw the enormous ox and his driver. In her surprise she twirled her parasol around and around, right under Babe's nose.

The big blue ox couldn't help it. He lowered his head, and pawed the ground angrily. Fire and smoke poured out from his nostrils. With a bellow of pain he rushed at the pink object and snatched it from the girl's hand. Then off he went like a tornado. He roared up and down the coast of British Columbia and the coast of Washington. The glacier dragged behind him like a driverless plow. It was several hours before they could calm him down. When at last they led him off to the stable, there lay a great gash in the earth. Puget Sound was dug. Not only Puget Sound, but the Hood Canal as well!

The biggest change Paul made in the map of North America was one of the first of all. It took place while he was building the Onion River Camp. He needed reservoirs for drinking water, both for his men and for the animals about the place. Babe, of course, drank a whole lake full every morning before breakfast. So the lumberjack dug the Great Lakes. He started with Lake Ontario. This proved to be too small to be practical. He moved a little farther west and dug Lake Erie, several sizes larger. These two little lakes did very well until his camp began to grow. When the Big Swede and Johnny Inkslinger joined his company he needed still larger reservoirs.

He dug Huron and Michigan, in the hope that they would prove to be enough. Not until he had finished the largest lake of all, Superior, did he have a really good water supply.

Babe and Brimstone Bill filled the lakes. They hauled water from the Atlantic Ocean on big sleds. Once Babe tripped over a small hill in the Huron Range. The sled turned over and spilled the big tank of water. Down to the south it poured in a rushing flood. Paul realized that the whole country would be flooded. Fields and towns and railroads would all be carried down to the Gulf of Mexico. To avoid disaster he grabbed up his spade. He ran ahead of the water, digging a channel for it to flow into. On either side of the ditch great spadefuls of earth were tossed into the air. They landed in long even piles, one to the east, one to the west. Paul Bunyan reached the Gulf just in time. The water spilled safely out into the ocean stream without doing any damage.

Yankee Doodle's Cousins

The ditch, as you may have guessed, is still filled with a great river, the Mississippi. The ridges of earth thrown up by Paul's spade are none other than the Rocky Mountains and the Appalachians. Wouldn't the map of North America be dull without these?

Glossary

A

Admiral: the chief officer of the navy.

Admiralty: the office in London that looks after the Royal Navy.

antics: pranks or tricks.

antlers: the horns of a stag.

artesian well: a deep well drilled straight down into the springs underground.

atone: to make up for something.

B

backwater: a small, shallow pond that flows into a stream or river.

balsam: a kind of evergreen tree.

Bang-All: the name of Mike Fink's rifle.

bass: a kind of fish.

bayou: a winding channel in the swamps of Louisiana.

Bébé: the French way of saying Babe.

Betsey: the name of Davy Crockett's rifle.

bit: a metal bar which, placed in the horse's mouth, connects the reins; part of the bridle.

blackguard: a wicked person.

blizzard: a very bad snowstorm.

block and tackle: a pulley; a system of ropes and pulleys which makes it possible to lift heavy things.

blockhouse: a log fortress.

bos'n: the boatswain; an officer on board ship.

bouquet: a bunch of flowers.

bowie knife: a long knife used by the pioneers, invented by Colonel James Bowie.

bronco: a small, wild horse of the Western plains; a mustang.

bruin: a bear.

buccaneer: a pirate; a sea robber.

bucksaw: a big saw attached to a wooden frame; used for sawing logs.

bullhead: a kind of fish.

bull's-eye: the center of a target.

bunkhouse: wooden house or shanty containing bunks for lumberjacks.

burgomaster: a high officer in a Dutch city; one of the important men in the town.

Glossary

C

calks: nails or bits of metal on the soles of boots to protect the leather and to prevent slipping.

canyon: a long, narrow gorge or ravine; the bed of a stream between high cliffs of rock.

cap (in *The Big Bear*): a small charge of powder or explosive which makes the gun fire.

cap (an oil well): to close an oil well with a heavy 'cap' of metal which prevents the oil from running off and being wasted.

capstan: a machine on shipboard which winds and unwinds the anchor chain.

caravel: a fleet of ships sailing together.

carcass: the body of an animal.

caribou: a large animal like a reindeer found in the Arctic regions of North America.

c'est-à-rire: French for 'What a joke!'

chaps: wide leather leggings the cowboys wear over their pants.

cider press: a machine that presses cider from apples.

cloven: split.

clue: a hint used in solving a mystery.

cobbler: a shoemaker.

comic opera: a funny play with music.

committee: a group of persons appointed to get something done.

Congress: the group of people who are elected by the citizens of the United States to go to Washington to make the laws.

corral: a pen for horses or cattle.

cotton batting: soft, thick rolls of cotton used in making quilts and stuffing for chairs, etc.

cove: a little bay or inlet.

coyote: a wild animal of the dog family, found on the Western prairies.

crest: the top, or peak, of a hill.

crisis: a turning point; usually a very serious time when things have to turn either for the better or for the worse.

critter: properly, a creature; a living thing.

crotch: a fork between two branches.

cruet: a bottle for holding vinegar or syrup.

curb: hold back.

cutaway coat: a formal coat for men.

cyclone: a very bad windstorm on the prairies.

cypress: an evergreen tree found in our Southern States.

D

Davy Jones's Locker: the bottom of the sea.

desperado: an outlaw; a bad-man.

distillery: a place where oil is made pure.

dory: a small rowboat.

doubloon: a Spanish gold coin.

Drainage Company: a company which

Glossary

makes a business of draining swamps.

draw: a tie.

drumstick: the leg of a chicken, or goose or turkey.

dude: a city fellow who tries to act like a cowboy; a greenhorn.

dungarees: work pants, usually made of blue denim.

dynamite: a high explosive.

E

Eminence (His): a title given to a bishop.

Execution Dock: a dock in London where pirates were hanged.

F

fang: a long sharp tooth of an animal.

fawn: a young deer.

fiend: a devil; a demon.

fire extinguisher: a machine for putting out fires.

fish fry: a party at which the refreshments are fried fish.

flanks: sides.

flats: a flat plain without grass or trees.

flinching: drawing away, as if in pain.

florist: a man who sells flowers.

flunkies: servants.

fore-bitts: the central part of a ship's deck, in front of the 'bitts,' posts for tying the cables; about the middle of the ship is what Stormalong means.

foreman: the boss of a group of workmen.

foundling: an orphan; a baby deserted by its parents and left for someone else to look after.

frontier: the last edge of settled country; the beginning of the wilderness.

frontlet: the forehead of a steer.

furl: wind up.

furrow: the track left by a plow.

G

gait: manner of walking.

galley: the kitchen on board ship.

geographers: men who write geographies; map-makers.

girders: steel beams.

glacier: big mass of ice; river of ice.

Governor General: the King's officer in Canada.

greenhorn: an ignorant fellow.

gun shy: afraid of the noise made by a gun.

gusher: an oil well from which the oil spouts into the air.

H

habitants: French-Canadian farmers.

hangar: a big shed for airplanes.

hard-tack: hard, dry crackers used on ships.

harpoon: a spear with a rope tied to one end; the rope is fastened to the whale-boat, and the spear is thrown into the whale.

'*harricane country*': part of Kentucky and Tennessee, sometimes swept by bad windstorms, or hurricanes.

high-brow: very dignified and learned; highly educated.

hobnail: heavy nail in the sole of a boot.

hoe-down: a square-dance party.

hoist sail: raise sail.

hold: space below the deck of a ship in which the cargo is stored.

hull: the outer walls of a ship without decks or masts or cabins, etc.

Hunkie: a person who works in the steel mills; most of the 'Hunkies' came to this country from southern Europe, and took their name from Hungary, one of the countries from which they came.

hurricane: a bad windstorm.

I

ingot mold: a hollow shape into which metal is poured; when the metal cools off and hardens it takes the shape of the mold.

inquisitive: curious; nosy.

instinct: a natural feeling or knowledge, like that of the animals.

interior: the inside.

irresistible: too strong to be resisted.

J

jerked beef: meat dried by hunters for their use on trips and during poor seasons.

johnny-cake: New England corn bread.

K

kid: a young goat.

L

lair: a den; home of a wild animal.

lariat: a cowboy's rope; a lasso.

lasso: a cowboy's rope; a lariat.

laughing-stock: a joke; someone who has been made to look foolish to his friends.

lean-to: a crude shanty or shelter, built of logs leaning against a ridgepole.

levee: a dike or bank to protect a town from floods.

liniment: ointment to cure aches and pains.

locks: the spaces between the gates of a canal; here boats are raised or lowered from one level to another.

log-drive: the job of floating the logs downstream to the sawmill.

logging: the business of cutting down trees.

long-barreled gun: a rifle with a very long barrel, used by the pioneers and explorers.

lumberjack: a man who works in the lumber camps cutting down trees.

Glossary

M

mainsail: the main sail of a sailing ship.

mansion: a large, grand house.

marksman: a man who is skilled at shooting a rifle.

maroon: to leave someone alone on a desert island.

mash: pulp; all that is left of apples after the cider has been pressed out.

maverick: a steer that has no brand; a wild outlaw.

medicine man: a person who is thought by the Indians to have magic powers.

meerschaum: a white clay from which pipes are made.

merchantman: a ship which carries merchandise; a freighter.

mine-patch: a little village around a coal mine.

minstrel: a singer or a poet; a man who tells stories in ballad form.

molten: melted.

mustang: a small half-wild horse of the Western prairies.

mutineer: a sailor who revolts against the officer of his ship.

N

Nantucket sleigh-ride: a wild ride in a whale-boat; after a whale has been harpooned, he swims madly away trying to shake off the harpoon and pulling the little whale-boat after him.

navigate: to sail.

new-fangled gadget: a new invention; some strange and new machine.

nugget: rough lump of ore containing gold.

O

open-hearth: a furnace for melting iron ore to make steel.

orator: a public speaker.

orchardman: a man who grows trees for a living.

P

parasol: a sunshade.

Parliament: the council of men who make the laws in England and Canada; very like our Congress in some ways.

passenger pigeon: a wild pigeon that once lived in the forests of North America.

patron saint: the saint who looks after a certain person or group of persons.

peddler: a man who sells things from door to door.

le petit: French for 'little one.'

Petrified Forest: a forest in Arizona; the trees are so old that they have turned to stone.

pickaninny: a Negro baby.

pile-driver: a machine which drives piles, or big posts, into the earth.

pioneer: an explorer or an early settler.

plot: a bit of ground.

Glossary

plugged nickel: a nickel that isn't worth anything as money.

poke bonnet: an old-fashioned lady's bonnet.

polka: a lively dance.

port: the left side of a ship.

possessions: belongings.

pounds of gold: English money, worth about five dollars.

prairie schooner: a covered wagon in which the pioneers traveled to the West.

privateer: a pirate; a man who attacks the ships of his country's enemies and keeps their cargoes.

prize: a ship captured by a pirate.

prophecy: telling what will happen in the future.

Provincial Governor: the governor of a Canadian province.

prow: the front or beak of a ship.

prune: to trim a tree, to take off its dead branches.

pueblo: a Southwestern Indian village of mud huts.

R

ragamuffin: a ragged, dirty child.

range: grazing lands.

reply in kind: to give someone the same treatment he gives you.

resent: to feel angry about something.

rickety: shaky, weak in the joints.

ridgepole: the pole that runs along the top of a roof, where the two sides join.

rigging: the ropes and masts of a ship.

ring-tailed squealer: an imaginary animal that sounded fierce to Mike Fink.

rivet: a nail or bolt that holds metal plates together.

rodeo: a cowboys' circus; a Wild West show.

round-up: gathering in the cattle from the range to brand them, etc.

roustabout: a man who works on the wharves and levees of the Mississippi River.

S

sacrifice: give up, or offer to a god.

sagebrush: a desert plant.

Saint Nicholas: the patron saint of Dutch children; like our Santa Claus he brings presents at Christmas time.

salt lick: a place where animals come to lick salt from rocks.

'Salt River roarer': another of Mike Fink's imaginary wild animals.

sapling: a young tree.

schooner: a sailing ship with two or more masts.

Scripture: the Bible.

scrub: low bushes in a thicket.

semicircle: a half circle.

settlement: a newly started town.

shaft: a tunnel, generally up and down, that leads to a mine.

'Shakes': the Western part of Tennessee and Kentucky.

Glossary

sheriff: an officer of the law.

shied (of a horse): bucked or reared.

short order: food that can be fixed quickly and easily, like hamburger and sandwiches.

shroud: a burial garment.

side-kicking: a cowboy term for a horse's bucking.

sign on: to hire a crew for a ship.

six-shooter: a gun that shoots six times between loadings.

skillet: an iron frying pan.

sky-walking: another cowboy term for a horse's bucking.

sledge: a heavy hammer.

sloop: a small sailing ship with one mast.

smuggling: bringing things into the country without paying the proper tax on them.

snags: rocks and tree stumps hidden under the surface of a river.

snuff: powdered tobacco.

sod shanty: a crude hut built of blocks of earth, sometimes with grass still growing from the blocks.

sombrero: a cowboy hat with a broad brim.

squid: a small octopus.

squire: the most important man in the county.

starboard: the right side of a ship.

steam crane: a large machine, operated by steam, for lifting heavy objects.

steam shovel: a big machine for digging, operated by steam.

stoke: to fill with coal.

store clothes: clothes bought at a store and worn on special occasions.

sugarbush man: a man who lives in the maple-sugar country.

sulphur springs: springs of water which contain sulphur.

superstition: a belief in something that you can't understand.

surveyor: a man who makes maps and works out the boundary lines between pieces of land.

T

tattoo: a picture or design marked on a person's skin.

'taxes and politics': things Congressmen usually talk about.

tender: a small boat that carries things between a large ship and the shore.

tepee: an Indian's tent or wigwam.

thaw: melting of the ice in the spring.

thresh: separate the kernel of grain from the straw.

tidal wave: a huge wave, so big that people think it must be caused by an earthquake under the sea.

timber: trees or lumber.

toreador: a bullfighter.

tornado: a bad windstorm.

train: a group of followers.

turpentine hills: hills covered with

Glossary

pine trees, from whose sap the turpentine is made.

turquoise: a stone found in the South-west.

V

vaquero: a Mexican cowboy.

varmint: pioneer slang for any low form of animal, generally a snake.

vein: a long layer of coal or metal in the rock.

vision: wonderful idea, or dream.

volunteer: a person who offers to do something.

W

wake: the waves that spread out behind a boat.

weigh anchor: pull up the anchor.

whaling station: ports from which whaling ships sail.

Y

Yankee clipper: a fast sailing ship that sailed from New England in the old days.

yarbs: herbs, plants used for medicine.